Y0-AIE-577

Inflammation

A SCOPE® PUBLICATION

Graeme B. Ryan, M.B., B.S., Ph.D.

*Associate Professor,
Department of Pathology, Harvard Medical School,
Boston, Massachusetts*

Guido Majno, M.D.

*Professor and Chairman,
Department of Pathology, University of Massachusetts
Medical School, Worcester, Massachusetts*

Upjohn

Published by The Upjohn Company, Kalamazoo, Michigan

Copyright© 1977 The Upjohn Company, Kalamazoo, Michigan.
All rights reserved. No part of this work may be reproduced or utilized in any form or by any means, electronic or mechanical, including photocopying, recording, or by an information storage and retrieval system, without permission in writing from the publisher.

8801-11 R4

Reprinted 1983, 1985, 1986, 1987

Library of Congress Card Number: 76-19187

Contents

- page 5 **Introduction**
- 6 **Historic Highlights**
- 10 **The Acute Inflammatory Response**
- 12 **Increased Vascular Permeability**
- 12 Inflammatory Swelling
- 12 The Capillary Wall as a Filter
- 14 Mechanisms of Vascular Leakage
- 16 Histamine-Type Vascular Leakage
- 19 Leakage By Direct Vascular Injury
- 21 Formation of the Exudate: An Overview
- 23 Types of Exudate
- 23 Effects of the Inflammatory Focus
- 24 **Leukocytic Infiltration**
- 24 Leukocytic Sticking
- 26 Leukocytic Emigration (Diapedesis)
- 28 What Kinds of Leukocytes Emigrate in Acute Inflammation – and When?
- 29 Chemotaxis
- 32 Mechanisms Involved In Leukocyte Chemotaxis
- 32 Chemotaxis *In Vivo*
- 33 **Phagocytosis**
- 38 **Defects of Leukocytic Function**
- 38 Neutropenia
- 38 Disorders of Migration and Chemotaxis
- 40 Disorders of Phagocytosis
- 40 Disorders of Microbicidal Mechanisms
- 42 **Mediators of Inflammation**
- 43 Factors Released From Plasma
- 43 *Kinin System*
- 44 *Complement System*
- 47 *Clotting System*
- 47 Hereditary Angioneurotic Edema
- 48 Factors Released From Tissues
- 48 *Vasoactive Amines*
- 51 *Acidic Lipids*
- 52 *Lysosomal Components*
- 55 *Lymphocyte Products*
- 56 *Other Tissue-Derived Mediators*
- 57 The Role of Mediators In Inflammatory Responses
- 58 **Chronic Inflammation**
- 59 Forms of Chronic Inflammation
- 66 **Systemic Effects of Inflammation**
- 66 Fever
- 67 Leukocytosis
- 69 **Inflammation – The Healing Phase**
- 72 Wound Healing
- 74 **Inflammation – A Two-Edged Sword**
- 75 Inflammation and Cancer
- 76 **Conclusion**
- 78 Bibliography
- 80 Acknowledgments

Introduction

About three billion years ago, when life appeared on this planet, death came with it – and presumably also injury. Only science fiction could tell us how the first free-swimming cells were injured; but whatever it was that hurt them – the heat of lava, falling rocks, or lightning – they had to learn how to repair their microscopic wounds. They also had to deal with bacteria, although one of the earliest battles between cells and bacteria seems to have ended in a permanent alliance: according to a current, well-founded theory, the bacteria settled inside the cells and became mitochondria. In the meantime, the cells developed techniques for eating and drinking *(phagocytosis* and *pinocytosis)*. Just as wild beasts use their jaws to fight as well as to feed themselves, it is quite likely that the first free cells learned to deal with obnoxious bacteria simply by swallowing them. When multicellular organisms appeared, the response to injury began to show a certain subdivision of labor among different cell types. Lost cells were replaced by new ones *(regeneration)*, while the process of cleanup and the defense against bacteria were taken over by specialized cells – professional phagocytes, as it were. This elementary stage of the defense and healing process is still visible in invertebrates. In higher animals, and typically in mammals, in which the internal environment is far more specialized, local injury brings about a response of even greater complexity. This is due primarily to the presence of blood vessels. Healing of injured cells (still a little-known process), cellular regeneration, and phagocytosis all take place as in lower animal forms. In addition, the blood vessels take part in the process by a series of active, automatic changes; they become wider and pour fluid, phagocytes, and other specialized cells into the problem area, whatever the injurious agent may have been. In many cases, the tissue reaction is further complicated by a superimposed allergic response, whereby cells and blood vessels react specifically against a certain class of substances recognized as foreign, especially proteins. The overall reaction brought about by local injury, and especially the vascular reaction, can be quite spectacular; a patch of skin or mucosa can swell up and become red, hot, and painful. The similarity with an "internal fire" is only too obvious, hence the ancient, empirical name of *inflammation*.

Today, the term inflammation is used in a very broad sense, even for situations in which the typical "flaming" effect is not visible to the naked eye. A completely satisfying definition of inflammation is not available and probably not necessary. For working purposes, however, let us say that *inflammation is a process typical of vascularized tissues, whereby fluid and white blood cells accumulate at a site of injury. The overall biologic significance of inflammation is that of a defense mechanism.* The reasons for this statement, and some exceptions to the rule, will become apparent in this monograph.

Graeme B. Ryan

Guido Majno

Historic Highlights

The concept of inflammation has a very colorful history, the main reason being that it is closely bound to the history of *infection,* an ancient and perhaps perennial human problem. Infection, by the way, is not at all the same as inflammation. Infection means that bacteria, viruses, or fungi have invaded the tissues – this usually causes inflammation. As we shall see later, inflammation is not always due to infection. Just consider a bee sting: it causes inflammation, but usually there is no infection.

A word that can be translated as "inflammation" is used several times in the Smith Papyrus, a scroll written in Egypt around 1650 B.C., and derived from an original that was perhaps 1000 years older. In hieroglyphs, the word looks as shown in Figure 1 – and if the missing vowels are filled in (for want of a better guess) as "e"s, it reads *shememet*. The last sign at the right is not to be read; it is called a "determinative," and its purpose was to give the general idea of the preceding word, "tree" ◊ , "shrub" ⊮ , "mineral" o o o , "watery" ∿∿∿∿ , etc. For shememet, the determinative ⌘ is a flaming brazier, with smoke rising and curving down again; it conveys the idea of "hot thing." So there is no doubt that the Egyptians had a word similar to inflammation. In the Smith Papyrus, this word is used in connection with wounds, presumably infected wounds.

In Greek medicine at the time of Hippocrates (460-380 B.C.), inflammation was called *phlegmoné*, which meant something like "the burning thing" (the word survives in *phlegmon*, a particularly vicious, fast-spreading form of infection). In those days, and throughout antiquity, a common clinical example of inflammation was an infected wound: for obvious reasons, most wounds became infected, and healed only after a period of suppuration (pus formation). This fact misled our ancient predecessors into believing that suppuration is a necessary step toward healing; hence two practical conclusions that now make us shudder: *a*) because pus was a kind of "badness" coming out of the wound, suppuration had to be encouraged – the more, the better; and *b*) since pus was thought to arise, somehow, through a decay of the blood, the best way to stop this decay was to remove as much blood as possible – the more, the better. The reasoning sounded so logical that it lasted about 4,000 years. Now imagine the disastrous consequences of this "cure." It is bad enough to bleed a patient suffering from any

Figure 1. Smith Papyrus, circa 1650 B.C. Hieroglyphs read *shememet,* translated as "inflammation."

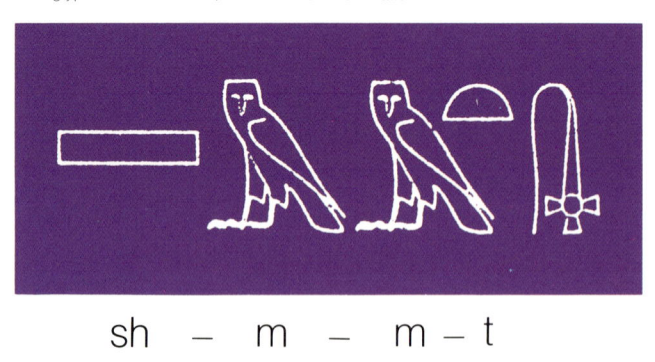

Figure 2. Julius Cohnheim (1839-1884), in his studies on the pathology of inflammation, pointed out the important part played by the small blood vessels. He emphasized that venules rather than capillaries deserved most attention.

form of infection (for the bodily defenses depend so much on the blood itself), but the pernicious logic of blood-letting led to even greater absurdities. Up until three or four generations ago, it was standard practice *to bleed even the wounded on the battlefield, to prevent "inflammation" of their wounds!* Hopefully, none of the mistakes that we are now making is as bad as this one.

The practical Romans added little to Greek medical theory (although, with their magnificent military hospitals, they were ahead of the Greeks). However, it was a Roman writer of the first century A.D., Cornelius Celsus, who provided us with a clinical definition of inflammation so precise that we have not yet improved upon it. The major signs of inflammation, says Celsus, are four: *RUBOR ET TUMOR CUM CALORE ET DOLORE*, "redness and swelling with heat and pain." We now call these the "cardinal signs." This famous definition occurs in an encyclopedia that covers a range of subjects from war to agriculture. Where Celsus took it from we do not know; but the fact remains that even today, if you do not learn it, you might miss a question on a multiple-choice exam.

No real progress was made in the understanding of inflammation from antiquity until the mid-1800s – with one exception. Just before he died in 1793, John Hunter, a Scottish surgeon-scientist, wrote a great treatise on *Blood, Inflammation, and Gunshot Wounds*, in which he maintained that inflammation was not a disease, but rather a "salutary reaction." This was definitely a step in the right direction, but to understand the nature of this "salutary reaction," little could be accomplished without the microscope. Although the microscope was invented in the early 1600s, it was not systematically applied to medical research until the early 1800s.

Rudolph Virchow (1821-1902), the founder of modern cellular pathology, contributed surprisingly little to the understanding of inflammation. However, it was one of his pupils, Julius Cohnheim, who wrote the first key paper on the subject in 1867 (Figure 2). In those days, efficient microtomes did not exist; in fact, paraffin embedding did not exist, and even the staining of tissue samples was unusual. So Cohnheim, like many others before him, studied natural, thin membranes, such as the mesentery and the tongue of the frog, and he studied them *in the living state* (Figure 3). It was especially the frog mesentery that gave him the clue to the basic phenomena of inflammation. As the mesentery became irritated under the microscope (simply by being exposed), Cohnheim noticed a series of changes in the blood vessels. First, there was a dilatation of the arterioles and an acceleration of blood flow in all the vascular network. A few minutes later the flow became slower than normal. White blood cells began to line the wall of the venules, as if glued there, while the red cells floated past them. Then, slowly – and this was the greatest surprise – some of the attached white blood cells crept across the wall of the venules and ended up in the extravascular spaces (a process now called diapedesis). In some of the venules, the flow stopped altogether; the red blood cells were tightly packed as if the plasma had been lost. Fifteen years after his first observations, Cohnheim published an afterthought on this point, adding that the plasma had escaped *because the permeability of the blood ves-*

Figure 3. The tongue of a live frog, one of Cohnheim's favorite microscopic preparations.

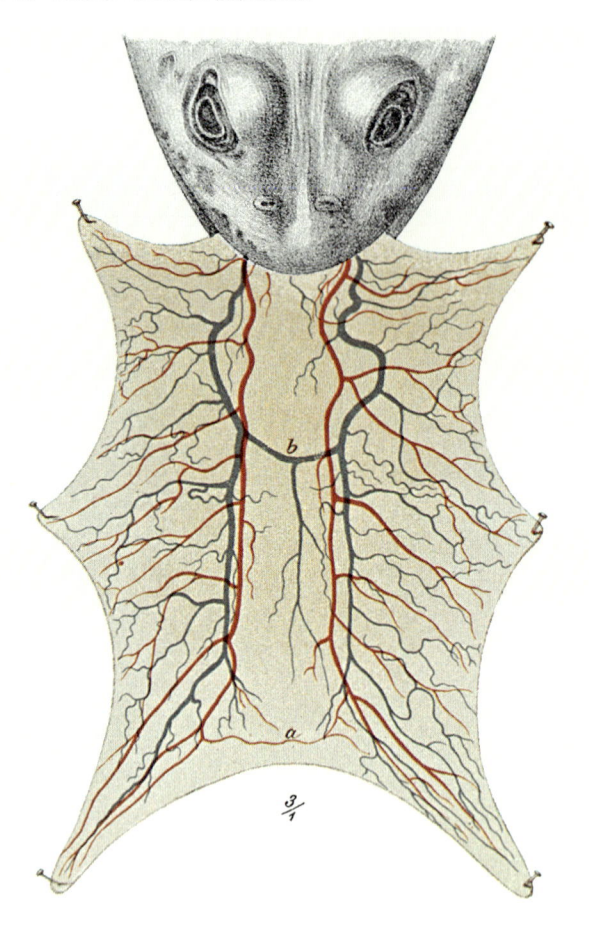

Figure 4. Elie Metchnikoff (1845-1916) demonstrated the nature of phagocytosis as a defense mechanism against invading microorganisms.

sels had been increased: another major step in the understanding of inflammation.

All these changes, wrote Cohnheim, could explain the four cardinal signs of Celsus; the vasodilatation could account for the *rubor;* the increased flow for the *calor;* the exudation of fluid for the *tumor;* and, although the frog could not speak, the *dolor* could be assumed. Few papers in the history of pathology had the clarity and the impact of this one.

Then a rather amusing thing happened. Toward the end of the 1800s, German treatises of pathology sprang up in good numbers and, in dealing with inflammation, they all mentioned the classic, traditional four cardinal signs of Celsus. But in 1882 a fifth sign crept in, *functio laesa,* "disturbed function," meaning that if an organ is inflamed, it does not function as it should. So far, nothing extraordinary. For a few years, this fifth sign remained fatherless; then one German *Handbuch* attributed it to Galen, and the legend has been retained unto our days. No self-respecting textbook of pathology could fail to mention the four cardinal signs of Celsus, plus the fifth sign of Galen. Now Galen, who lived in Rome about a century and a half after Celsus, wrote more about medicine than almost anybody else in the whole of history. But if you should take the trouble of looking through the 22 volumes of Galen's complete works, you would find no discussion of the four signs of Celsus, and surely no addition of a fifth sign. Galen was a haughty Greek, and although he lived in a Roman world, he did not quote Roman authors; some even believe that he never bothered

Figure 5. Two views of a frog leukocyte which has ingested an anthrax bacillus (stained). Metchnikoff, 1891.

to learn Latin (this may be going too far). The bare fact is that *the fifth cardinal sign was added not by Galen, but by Virchow,* in his *Cellular Pathology,* published in 1858. In those days Virchow's fame was so great that anything he wrote, or even said, became instant pathologic gospel. What apparently happened is that the author of a *Handbuch* remembered hearing about the fifth sign somewhere by some top authority, and somehow his memory switched from Virchow to Galen. And then the legend persisted. We mention it here simply to caution you about "classic" quotations, medical or otherwise, that are handed down from book to book and never checked — this one for nearly one hundred years.

Now, returning to Cohnheim: although he did describe the emigration of white blood cells, he did not know why these cells emigrated or what they might do once they were outside. It was a Russian biologist, Elie Metchnikoff (Figure 4), who unraveled that part of the problem. Working in Sicily where he had escaped as a political refugee, and using living, transparent invertebrates for his microscopic studies, he discovered that there were cells capable of engulfing foreign matter, including bacteria (Figure 5). He called this process *phagocytosis,* "cellular eating," and since some of the white cells in the blood of higher animals also behaved as phagocytes, he concluded that the purpose of inflammation was perfectly obvious — bringing phagocytes to the injured area to engulf invading bacteria or any other foreign matter.

Metchnikoff's major paper appeared in 1882. During the same period, antibodies and "antitoxins" were discovered. Thus, another facet of inflammation became understandable: the increased permeability of the blood vessels allowed antibodies to pour out rapidly into infected tissues to participate in the local defense. Since then, immunologic processes have become tightly interwoven with the biology of inflammation. These processes and the cellular mechanisms of increased permeability, as well as phagocytosis, have recently been explained through the use of the electron microscope. But one important lesson remains from the work of the pioneers. Cohnheim's discovery of leukocytic diapedesis and Metchnikoff's discovery of phagocytosis were made not on microscopic sections, but on natural, transparent tissues — more difficult to study, but with the added dimension of life.

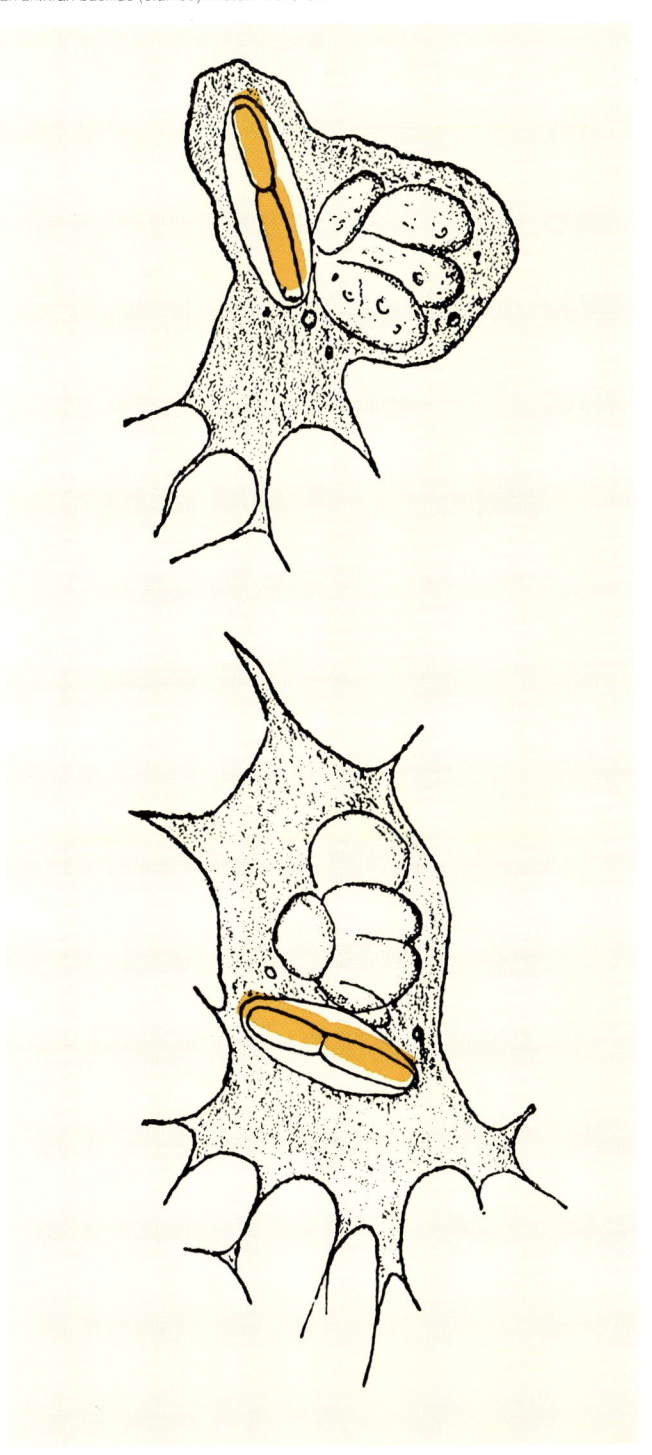

The Acute Inflammatory Response

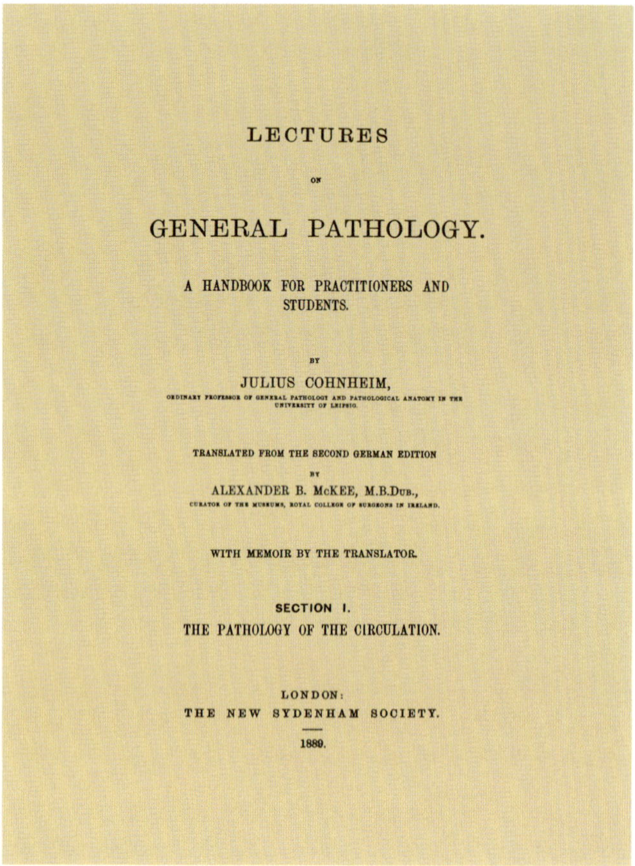
LECTURES

ON

GENERAL PATHOLOGY.

A HANDBOOK FOR PRACTITIONERS AND STUDENTS.

BY

JULIUS COHNHEIM,

ORDINARY PROFESSOR OF GENERAL PATHOLOGY AND PATHOLOGICAL ANATOMY IN THE UNIVERSITY OF LEIPSIG.

TRANSLATED FROM THE SECOND GERMAN EDITION

BY

ALEXANDER B. McKEE, M.B.DUB.,

CURATOR OF THE MUSEUMS, ROYAL COLLEGE OF SURGEONS IN IRELAND.

WITH MEMOIR BY THE TRANSLATOR.

SECTION I.

THE PATHOLOGY OF THE CIRCULATION.

LONDON:

THE NEW SYDENHAM SOCIETY.

1889.

Figure 6. Title page of Cohnheim's book on General Pathology.

In 1888, Sir John Scott Burdon-Sanderson wrote: "*The process of inflammation is the succession of changes which occurs in a living tissue when it is injured, provided that the injury is not of such a degree as at once to destroy its structure and vitality.*" As a definition, this statement is perhaps a little long-winded, but it serves to stress that inflammation consists of an overlapping succession of events – that is a *process*, not a *state*.

For the best description of this process (following injury to the frog mesentery), we go back to Cohnheim (Figure 6):

"*The first thing you notice in the exposed vessels is a dilatation which occurs chiefly in the arteries, then in the veins, and least of all in the capillaries. With the dilatation which is gradually developed, but which during the space of fifteen to twenty minutes has usually attained considerable proportions (often exceeding twice the original diameter) there immediately sets in in the mesentery an* acceleration of the bloodstream, *most striking again in the arteries, but very apparent in the veins and capillaries also. Yet this acceleration never lasts long; after half an hour or an hour, or sometimes after a shorter or longer interval, it invariably gives place to a decided* retardation, *the velocity of the stream falling more or less below the normal standard, and so continuing as long as the vessels occupy their exposed situation.*"

Cohnheim describes here the early onset of vascular dilatation, accompanied first by accelerated blood flow and then by slowing of flow. (*Note:* Most of the vessels that he called "veins," and probably some of his "capillaries," are now called *venules* – these range in diameter from around 10 to 100 microns.)

"*This stage having been reached, the vessels are seen to be all of them very wide; a multitude of capillaries which were formerly hardly perceptible can now be clearly distinguished ...But it is the veins rather than the capillaries that attract the notice of the observer; for slowly and gradually there is developed in them an extremely characteristic condition;* the originally plasmatic zone becomes filled with innumerable colourless corpuscles. *The plasmatic zone of the veins, you will remember, is always occupied by scattered colourless blood-corpuscles, which, owing to their globular form and low specific gravity, are driven into the periphery of the stream, and whose adhesiveness makes it difficult for them to escape from the wall once they have come into contact with it...the colourless cells of the plasmatic layer remain stationary at most for a time, they then advance a little, and perhaps make another short halt, and so on. Yet this does not lessen the striking con-*

trast presented by the central column of red blood-corpuscles, flowing in an uninterrupted stream of uniform velocity, and the peripheral layer of resting colourless cells; the internal surface of the vein appears paved with a single but unbroken layer of colourless corpuscles without the interposition at any time of a single red one. It is the separation of the white from the red corpuscles that gives the venous stream in these cases that characteristic appearance, anything analogous to which you will look for in vain in the other vessels."

The principal event that Cohnheim is describing during this period is that large numbers of white cells ("colourless corpuscles") show margination to the periphery of the red cell stream and into the plasmatic zone. The leukocytes are probably pushed to the periphery of the stream because the red cells aggregate together into "rouleaux" as slowing of flow occurs. Margination brings the leukocytes into contact with the venular wall – and here they stick to the endothelium (this is called pavementing). Incidentally, slowing of flow and eventual narrowing of the plasmatic zone result from the loss of fluid that occurs from the vessel – by increased vascular permeability.

"But the eye of the observer hardly has time to catch all the details of the picture before it is fettered by a very unexpected occurrence. Usually it is a vein with the typical peripheral arrangement of the white corpuscles, but sometimes a capillary, that first displays the phenomenon. A pointed projection is seen on the external contour of the vessel wall; it pushes itself further outwards, increases in thickness, and the pointed projection is transformed into a colourless rounded hump; this grows longer and thicker, throws out fresh points, and gradually withdraws itself from the vessel wall, with which at last it is connected only by a long thin pedicle. Finally this also detaches itself, and now there lies outside the vessel a colourless, faintly glittering, contractile corpuscle with a few short processes and one long one, of the size of a white blood-cell, and having one or more nuclei, in a word, a colourless blood-corpuscle. While this is taking place at one spot, the same process has been carried on in other portions of the veins and capillaries. Quite a large number of white blood-cells have betaken themselves to the exterior of the vessels, and these are constantly followed by fresh ones, whose place in the peripheral layer is immediately occupied by others. Like every stage of the entire process on from the moment of exposure, these phenomena may develop either rapidly or slowly; at one time the earliest emigration very quickly succeeds the pavementing; at another an hour or more may pass without anything happening to draw attention to the contour of a single vein or capillary. In any case the final result, after six or eight or more hours have elapsed, will be the enclosure of all veins, small and large, of the mesentery or wound of the tongue with several layers of colourless blood-corpuscles. These fence in the veins, in the interior of which the previously described conditions continue, namely, the peripheral arrangement of the colourless cells and the central unbroken flow of red blood-corpuscles. Nothing analogous has occurred in connection with the arteries, their contour has remained smooth as before, nor can a solitary corpuscle, red or white, be discovered on their outer surfaces, except of course such as may have reached them from neighbouring veins."

This is a beautiful account of leukocytic emigration (also called *diapedesis*).

"Keeping pace with this exodus, emigration, or, as it is also called, extravasation of corpuscular elements there occurs an increased transudation of fluid, in consequence of which the meshes of the mesentery, or the tissues of the tongue, are infiltrated and swell. But this is not all. The extravasated colourless corpuscles distribute themselves, in proportion as their numbers increase, over a large area, forsaking the neighbourhood of the vessels from which they were derived. The tissues become more and more densely packed with them, while the red cells, which have not the power of independent locomotion, remain seated in the vicinity of their capillaries, yet these also may be carried off by the stream of transudation. Soon a moment must arrive when the products of exudation and transudation can no longer be accommodated in the tissues. They now gain the free surface of the mesentery, and should the transuded fluid coagulate, as is the rule here, the final result of the processes just described will be the deposition on the mesentery, as well as on the intestine, of a fibrous pseudo-membrane, densely packed with colourless blood-corpuscles, and interspersed with isolated red cells."

Here, Cohnheim comments on two important events in inflammation: the transudation of fluid (we now call this *exudation of fluid*) and the movement of leukocytes away from the vessels. He also mentions that the tissues contain red cells (that have escaped from capillaries) and fibrin (derived from the coagulation of exudate fluid).

Cohnheim then goes on to describe the more drastic changes seen if a frog's tongue is painted with croton oil, silver nitrate, or some other caustic agent. In particular, he remarked how areas of severe injury are characterized by the presence of hemorrhages (accumulations of red cells in the tissues) and vascular stasis (cessation of blood flow).

Increased Vascular Permeability

Cohnheim used this series of observations to interpret the cardinal signs of inflammation. We quote from him again:

"On calling to mind the signs which make their appearance in a part of the body, in which the circulation and transudation has undergone the disturbances so often described, we find they are as follows. Such a part will be (1) reddened, owing to the overloading of all its vessels; this condition being complicated in severe forms with small, but numerous, hemorrhages. It will be (2) swollen, because of the increased vascular fulness, but especially because of the great increase of transudation. (3) It will be painful, owing to the pressure on, and dragging of, the nerves of sensation by the overfilled vessels and abundant transudation. (4) It will, if situated superficially, be warmer to the touch, because a more than normal amount of heat is supplied to it from within by the increased supply of blood. Lastly, (5) its function will be deranged, both by reason of the pressure to which the terminations of the motor and secretory nerves are subject from the transudation, and the so essentially altered blood-circulation, in particular the retardation of the capillary stream. Now these five symptoms are nothing more or less than the cardinal symptoms of acute inflammation, of which the first four - the fifth, the functio laesa, is in reality less a symptom than a resulting condition - had been already established by Celsus; and, despite the advance made in our knowledge of the processes, still serve best to characterise the condition of an inflamed part. We say that a finger or a foot, an ear or a knee, is acutely inflamed when it is red, swollen, hot, and painful. This notion of inflammation has been for ages held by the laity; and pathology cannot, as I have just said, better describe acute inflammation than by these symptoms."

Inflammation, then, can be subdivided into the following major events: 1) Changes in vascular caliber and blood flow, 2) Increased vascular permeability, 3) Infiltration of the tissues by leukocytes.

We cannot improve on Cohnheim's description of the changes in vascular caliber and blood flow. Let us now discuss the factors involved in the other two events.

Inflammatory Swelling

Swelling, the Celsian *tumor*, is always present to some degree in acute inflammation. In the very early stages — for the first few hours, and up to a day or two at most — it is brought about only by the accumulation of fluid in the tissues. But if the inflammatory state persists, another volume-increasing phenomenon will start and add itself to (or slowly replace) the flood of exudate: the production of new connective tissue. The mass of hyperplastic connective tissue will increase with time, until the inflammatory stimulus wears off. You will have to train your clinical touch to feel the difference between these two volume-increasing mechanisms beneath your fingertips, because this will help you to determine the age of the inflammatory lesion. Tissue swollen with fluid feels rather soft, whereas an increase of connective tissue gives a firm consistency. You will also have to train your eye to look for the swelling, which is not necessarily obvious. Sometimes it is so subtle that only careful observation will reveal it; an ancient and handy clinical trick is to compare symmetric joints (knees, elbows), for this may help you to notice that, on one side, a hollow or a skin crease has filled up.

Conversely, the swelling may be perfectly obvious, but how can you make sure that you are really dealing with an inflammatory swelling, and not with neoplastic swelling, for instance? Here again, ancient wisdom will guide you: just apply the notion of the four cardinal signs. If redness and heat are present, you may be relatively certain that you are dealing with inflammation and not with a neoplasm. But *pain* is very important, too. Inflammatory swellings almost always involve some pain, either spontaneous or induced by palpation; neoplasms are *usually* painless. Thus, when you palpate a local mass, and the patient gives no sign of pain at all, this is not necessarily good news.

Now for the mechanisms of swelling. In order to discuss the escape of fluid from the blood vessels, we will need a brief review of the normal mechanisms of exchange across the capillary wall.

The Capillary Wall as a Filter

The bulk of transendothelial exchange occurs in the so-called *microcirculation*, which includes arterioles, capillaries, and venules. This is the business end of the vascular network, the part that actually nourishes the tissues – which is, of course, the ultimate purpose of the whole vascular system. (Viewed in this light, the larger blood vessels are just plumbing: a system of tubes carrying the blood to and from the microcirculation.) The fine structure and, therefore, the physiology of the microcirculation vary tremendously from one tissue to another, because the local requirements are so different. The brain, for instance, because it is the most delicate of all tissues and is enclosed in a rigid box, must be especially protected against vascular leakage; whereas the bone marrow, which continually injects large numbers of its cells into the bloodstream, could scarcely be provided with a leak-proof microcirculation.

It helps to remember that there are three main types of capillary endothelium, each with certain variants. The most common is the *continuous* endothelium, in which the cells are attached to each other all around the periphery, with no grossly leaky points (this type is found in the capillaries of the skin, muscle, brain, lungs); in the *fenestrated* variety, the cells are riddled with small "fenestrae" or windows, which may be either open (as in the kidney glomerulus) or closed by a thin diaphragm (as in the endocrine and exocrine glands); the third is the *discontinuous*, in which there are openings between cells (as in the spleen and bone marrow).

As regards function, whatever you may have learned so far, we are sorry to say that a complete and satisfactory picture of physiologic transcapillary exchange is not yet available. The situation varies, of course, in different types of small vessels. For those with continuous endothelium, which pose the most complex problem, two facts are certain: a) *the endothelial layer acts as a filter,* b) *two physical mechanisms, diffusion and bulk flow, are involved in exchanges across the wall.* Even so, the details are not clear. In the first place, if it is true that the endothelium acts (in part at least) as a filter, how does this filter work? And is there any active transport? An eminent physiologist, John Pappenheimer, predicted a quarter of a century ago that there should be a system of pores with a diameter of 90 Å. The precise site of these pores has provoked some discussion. Morris Karnovsky injected horseradish peroxidase (molecular weight 40,000) intravenously into animals and described how the enzyme gained access to the tissue spaces by passing rapidly down the interendothelial junctions (Figure 7).

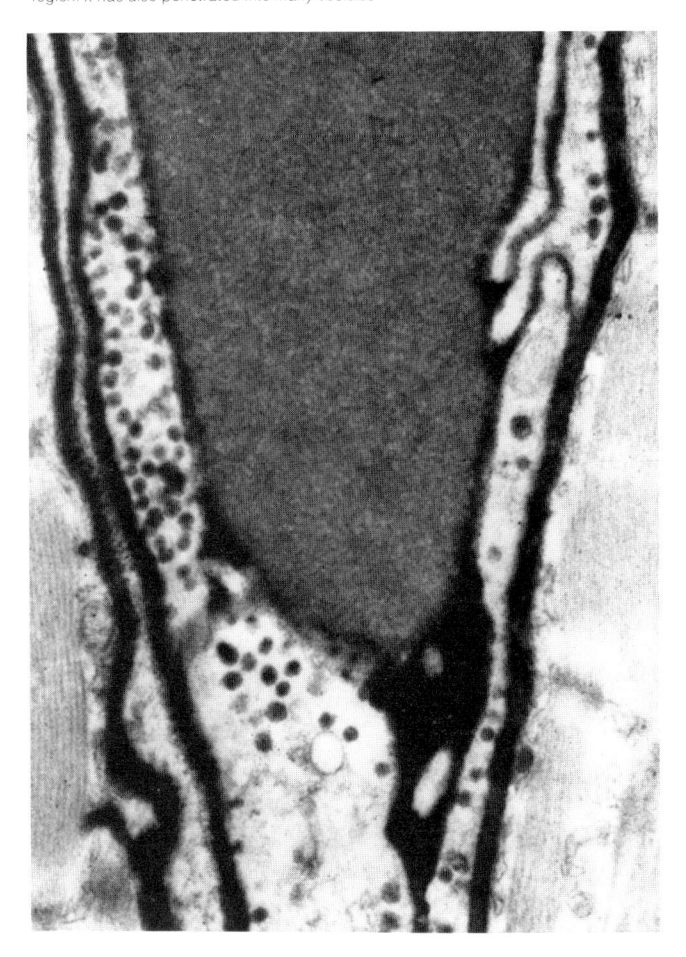

Figure 7. Horseradish peroxidase, used in this electron micrograph, oxidizes a heavy benzidine compound and produces an electron-dense substance (black). Here it has spread from the lumen through the endothelial junctions into the extravascular region. It has also penetrated into many vesicles.

On the other hand, George Palade (Nobel Prize, 1974) and his collaborators have suggested that much of the passage is accomplished via small pinocytic vesicles (Figure 7) which "ferry" pockets of plasma (or interconnect with one another) across the endothelial cell itself. The relative importance of these two mechanisms in different types of vessels, for different molecular sizes, is not yet clear. At this stage, it behooves students to keep an open mind.

There is better agreement about the physical forces acting across the endothelial wall, regulating fluid exchange. There are two opposing sets of forces: one set causes fluid to move out (one force pushes out, while another pulls from outside); the other set causes fluid to move in (one force pushes in, while another pulls

Figure 8.

**Physical Forces
Acting Across the Capillary Wall**
(approximate values in mm Hg)

causing fluid to move out		causing fluid to move in	
intravascular hydrostatic pressure (average)	23	osmotic pressure of plasma proteins	25
osmotic pressure of tissue proteins and mucopolysaccharides	10	hydrostatic tissue pressure	1 to 4
	≈ 33		≈ 26 to 29

from inside the vessel). The nature of these forces, and their approximate values in mm of mercury, are listed in Figure 8. Notice that the values represented in this figure correspond to the normal process of transudation. A *transudate* is the fluid that forms by ultrafiltration across the normal capillary wall; its quantity can be increased by raising the venous pressure, as in the classic experiment of placing a cuff around the root of the limb. Its protein content is relatively low (0.2 to 0.5 gm/100 ml in the case of subcutaneous circulatory edema, about 2% for the pleural fluid of heart failure). An *exudate* is the protein-rich fluid of inflammation; its protein content can be 4% to 5% and higher. (But the distinction between the two types of fluid is, of course, not a sharp one.)

Mechanisms of Vascular Leakage

Now we must try to understand why, in a focus of inflammation, the blood vessels should leak fluid.

The first and simplest explanation is that, inflammation being a response to injury, the injurious agent itself will sometimes damage the vessels and make them leak. This is perfectly correct, and we will call this *leakage by direct injury*. Oddly enough, it was not recognized until recently, although it had been postulated about a century ago by Cohnheim. However, leakage by direct injury is a purely accidental, passive, and mechanical phenomenon akin to bleeding; we cannot really call it a "response." It so happens that evolution brought about another and much more specific form of vascular leakage, an *active* phenomenon that occurs in the area of injury and especially around it. Certain blood vessels (venules) that were not directly injured are triggered by chemical messengers arising from damaged tissue, and they respond by becoming leaky. This we will call *indirect* or *histamine-type* leakage because the best known chemical messenger (or "mediator") of this kind is histamine.

Before going into further details, it will help to learn how vascular leakage can be studied and measured. In experimental animals, this is easily accomplished. The basic methods are three:

1) Measurement of dry weight – Assume that you want to know how much fluid accumulates in the skin after a burn. First you take a small piece of normal skin, you weigh it and then dry it in an oven for two days at 110°C. When you weigh it again, you will find that it has shrivelled up and lost about ¾ of its original weight. This means that its water content was 75%. When you repeat the procedure with inflamed skin, you will find that the loss of weight by drying is greater – meaning that the water content was higher.

2) "Blueing" – This strange term has now been generally accepted, at the expense of many thousands of white rats, rabbits and guinea pigs that became "blued rats," "blued rabbits," and "blued guinea pigs." The method works as follows: one injects intravenously a small, non-toxic dose of a dye, which has the property of becoming rapidly attached to the circulating albumin (this protein seems to be specialized for carrying other molecules, endogenous and exogenous). The two most suitable dyes happen to be blue – Evans blue (which is also used clinically for the determination of plasma volume) and trypan blue. As a result of the injection, the animal's circulating albumin turns blue. The bulk of the dye-protein complex will be retained in the bloodstream, but wherever the

Figure 9. Surface of a striated muscle. Diffuse leakage of trypan blue, 30 minutes after a local injection of histamine (rat cremaster muscle, magnified about 5 X).

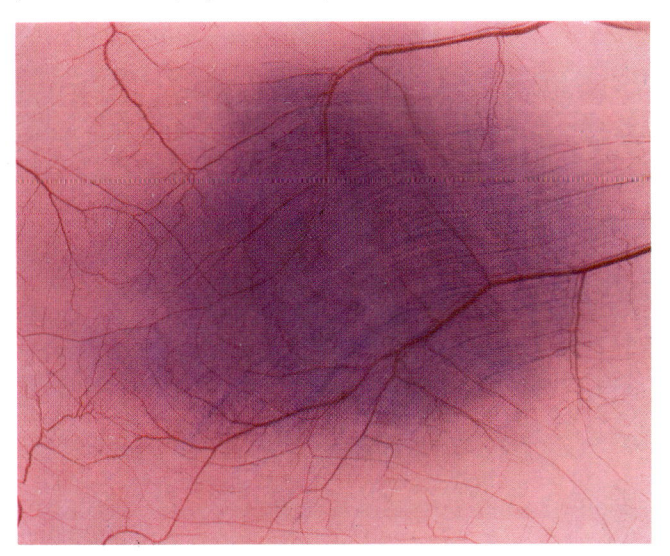

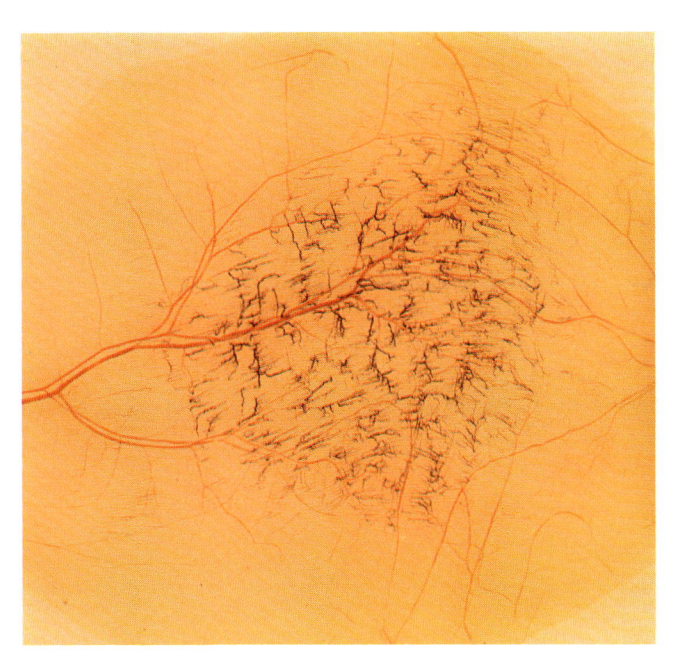

Figure 10. Vascular labelling with carbon black, one hour after a local injection of histamine, and an intravenous injection of India ink (rat cremaster muscle, magnified about 5 X).

endothelium is phagocytic, the so-called *littoral (shore)* phagocytes will recognize this material as foreign and begin to phagocytize it (primarily in the liver, spleen, and bone marrow). The remainder of the dye-protein complex will continue to circulate and seep out very, very slowly – as do all proteins – from all the capillaries except those of the brain, spinal cord, and peripheral nerves (where the interendothelial junctions are "tight"). Whenever the complex has oozed out of a capillary into the connective tissue, it may find its way into a lymphatic vessel, return to the bloodstream and start its trip all over again. Sooner or later, in one of its passages through the connective tissue, a macrophage will swallow the blue intruder, digest its protein, and store its undigestible blue in a phagosome or "residual body." Remember this odyssey of the blue molecules, because it can be duplicated by other passengers of albumin, such as drugs. The point of this story, as it regards experimental inflammation, is that immediately after the intravenous injection, while most of the dye-protein is still in the bloodstream, the skin of the animal still looks fairly pink (or light blue); but wherever there is a patch of leaky blood vessels, blue plasma pours out and a deep blue patch will appear (Figure 9). The effect is very striking, especially if the skin is dissected off and viewed from the deep side. One can also quantitate the leakage, either by extracting the dye or more simply by measuring the diameter of the blue spot. This method is very sensitive and widely used, but it has one drawback: while it shows the general area in which the leakage is occurring, it does not allow one to detect the individual leaking vessels. To accomplish this, a different method is employed: vascular labelling.

*3) **Vascular labelling*** – This method is even simpler than blueing. All that is necessary to identify a leaky vessel is to inject a few drops of India ink intravenously into the experimental animal. India ink is a suspension of carbon particles, which on electron micrographs are easily visible as dots 150 to 300 Å in diameter. As these particles circulate in the bloodstream, the endothelium ignores them, except where it is phagocytic. The littoral phagocytes are so effective that within an hour after the injection, the animal (whose skin had become a dull gray) is pink again. However, the liver and spleen are now jet black, and *wherever there is a leaky vessel in the microcirculation, it has become black or "labelled"* (Figure 10).

15

Figure 11. Schema of the "vascular labelling" effect. Note the filtering action of the basement membrane. *Top:* Normal venule with carbon black in lumen. *Middle:* Escape of plasma. *Bottom:* Labelling effect inside basement membrane.

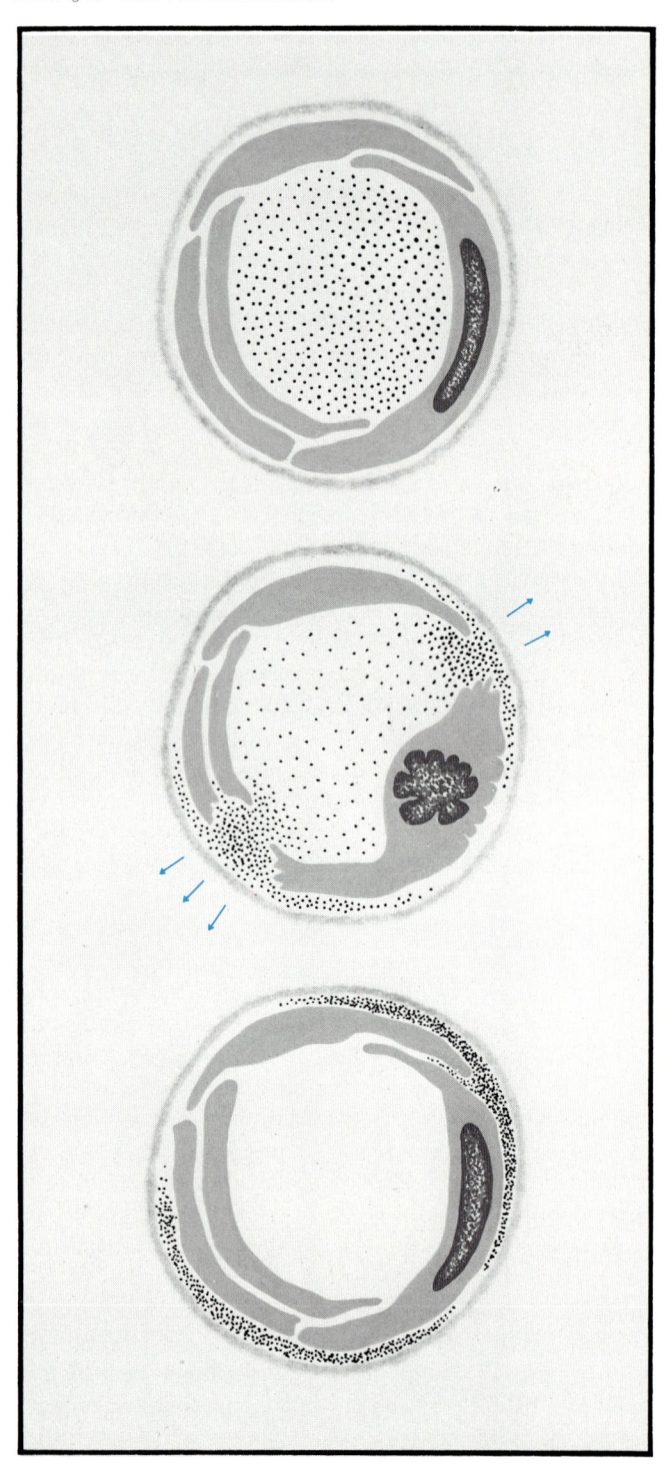

As shown by Majno and his colleagues in 1961, the mechanism is simple: assuming that there is a gap in the endothelium (within the microcirculation), plasma escapes out of the gap and filters across the basement membrane (Figure 11). Those particles too large to cross the membrane are retained, and the layer of carbon particles that pile up against it is so black that very small vessels become visible even to the naked eye. The method does not work with the blue dyes mentioned previously because the "blued" albumin molecules are too small to be retained by the basement membrane.

All this now sounds so very obvious; however, in retrospect, it was not easy to understand. India ink has been injected intravenously (in animals) for at least a half century. The blackening of blood vessels in and around areas of injury has been noticed by at least a dozen investigators. But the light microscope could not exactly discern what was happening at the cellular level, hence the phenomenon was interpreted as endothelial phagocytosis. The true significance of vascular labelling could be explained only by the better resolution of the electron microscope.

Histamine-Type Vascular Leakage

We shall begin by explaining this type of leakage because it is the most characteristic of inflammation.

The number and variety of chemical "mediators" capable of making blood vessels leak are so great that we had to give them a separate chapter (see p. 42). But, fortunately for medical students (and for researchers), there is also considerable unity in this variety. Most of the vasoactive mediators fall into a single family *with regard to their functional effects on the microcirculation.* The mediators cause the arterioles to dilate, and at the same time they induce a brief episode of vascular leakage which has three basic characteristics: 1) It occurs very fast (immediately upon application), 2) it lasts a short time (15 to 30 minutes), and 3) it affects primarily the venules (Figures 12, 13, 14).

This, then, is the typical behavior of histamine, serotonin, and the kinins (such as bradykinin). To visualize this short-lived episode of inflammatory edema, think of the sting of the nettle, which actually contains histamine.

Why does the endothelial layer become leaky? A purely morphologic answer was not difficult to find: gaps

Figure 12. Vascular labelling with carbon black, after a local injection of histamine (rat cremaster). There is no carbon in the wall of the arteriole (arrow). Note the progressive increase of carbon deposits on the venous side of microcirculation.

Figure 14. Detail of venules labelled with carbon black after a histamine injection (rat cremaster). The venules are labelled up to a diameter of 80 to 100 microns; the larger vein is not leaking, and therefore is not labelled.

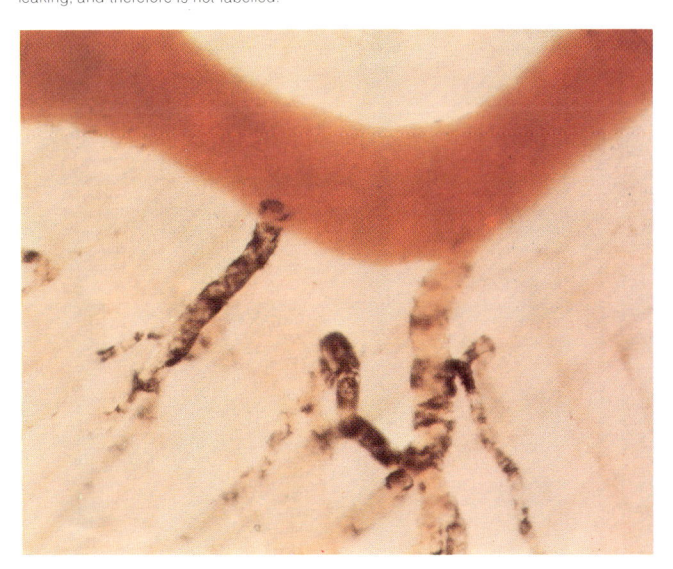

Figure 13a. Perfusion of a rat cremaster muscle with pure India ink (postmortem) to show the number of capillaries.

Figure 13b. Vascular labelling of another rat cremaster with carbon black after a local injection of histamine. Comparison with Fig. 13a [at same enlargement] shows that, although venules are labelled, most of the capillary bed is *not* labelled, because it is not leaking.

Figure 15. (top) One large and two small gaps in the endothelium of a venule in a rat cremaster, three minutes after a local injection of histamine and an intravenous injection of carbon black. Note folds in the endothelial nucleus (evidence of cellular contraction). The pericyte at top is raised by a mass of chylomicra; lipoproteins and carbon black are retained in the venular wall.

Figure 16. (bottom) Detail of two endothelial gaps in a venule in a rat cremaster, three minutes after a local injection of histamine and an intravenous injection of carbon black. Erythrocytes are protruding through the gaps. Thin pericytes and several layers of basement membrane contribute to retain particulate matter, especially carbon black and chylomicra (recognizable as faint grey masses).

(roughly a micron in width) appear between the endothelial cells (Figures 15, 16). Some of these gaps become plugged by platelets, but others remain open for 15 to 30 minutes and act as "sinks": plasma pours out, while chylomicrons and lipoprotein aggregates accumulate against the basement membrane, like impurities on a filter. Sometimes a part of a red blood cell is also caught in the sink (Figures 15, 16).

Incidentally, the existence of leaks between endothelial cells was noticed about 100 years ago. A German anatomist, Julius Arnold, injected intravenously (into frogs) a finely ground suspension of red mercuric sulfide, or cinnabar, a pigment also used for red tattoos. He observed that fine deposits of cinnabar appeared in the wall of certain venules (presumably injured ones), forming a lacelike pattern. Thereupon he killed the animals and perfused them with a solution of silver nitrate, which has the property of staining the outlines of the endothelial cells in black. With this ingenious method he found that the cinnabar was being deposited at or near the intercellular junctions of the endothelium (Figure 17).

Returning to our century, the next step in explaining histamine-type vascular leakage was not so easy. Why should a simple substance like histamine punch holes in the venules? The first thought was that the mediators somehow "unzipped" the intercellular junctions, but this has proved to be a false lead, at least unto this day. We will also allow you to test your own imagination; here is a hint: most, if not all, of the mediators that cause venules to leak can also cause smooth muscle cells to contract.

Using this hint, it was once proposed that the small *muscular* veins respond to the mediators by contracting, so that the smaller venules upstream (still devoid of a muscular coat) become stretched to the bursting point, and leak. But this, too, turned out to be wrong. The work of Majno's group suggested that what really happens in the nonmuscular venules is that the endothelial cells themselves contract, and as they do so, they pull away from each other. This is a very economical arrangement, because the substances that cause the venules to leak are the same as those that cause the small arterioles to dilate. It may seem bizarre at first that smooth muscle cells may respond in one vessel by shortening, and in another by relaxing, but this kind of bimodal behavior is commonly observed in pharmacology.

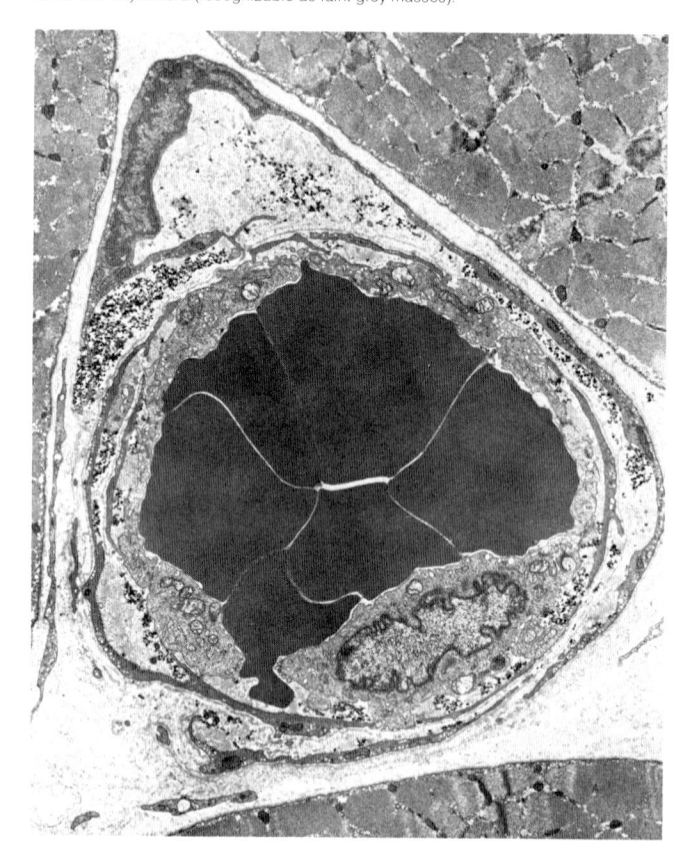

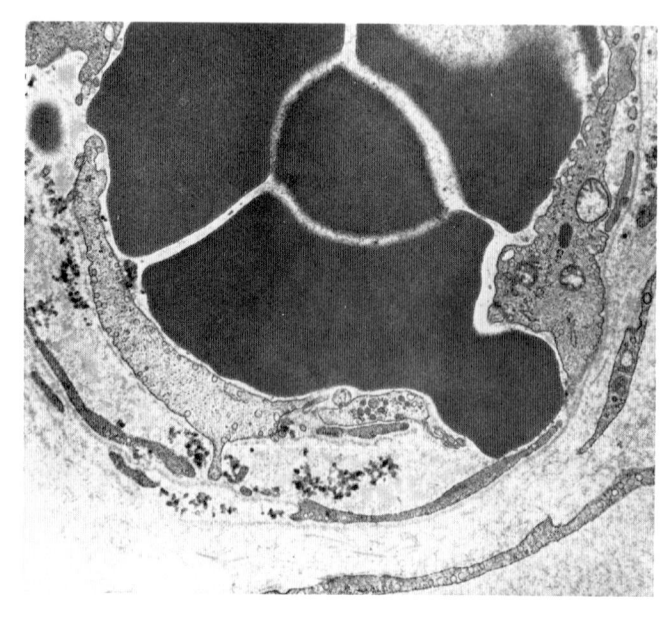

Figure 17. (top) Vascular labelling, as observed in the frog mesentery in 1875 by Julius Arnold.

Figure 18. (bottom) Contraction of endothelial cells as observed *in vivo* in a venule of the rat mesentery. *Upper section:* normal condition. *Lower section:* nine minutes after local application of histamine, a bulging endothelial cell is clearly visible (right).

Note also that this typically functional event, endothelial contraction, was demonstrated by a purely morphologic technique: electron microscopy. The observation was made rather accidentally. In studying the small blood vessels after a local injection of histamine, it was noticed that the nuclei of many endothelial cells had unusual shapes; they had rounded up and had developed many tight folds (Figure 15). This was interpreted as suggesting that the endothelial cells had shortened, and that in doing so, they had squeezed their nuclei from a long oval into a plump, more rounded shape. An actual contraction and rounding-up of the endothelial cells was later observed *in vivo*, in the venules of the living rat mesentery (Figure 18).

Up to this point, then, the story of the histamine-type mediators seems to unfold rather clearly. But one part remains to be worked out: why does the leakage response occur mainly in the venules? Why are the capillaries spared? With the electron microscope, one has the impression that the endothelial cells of the venules contain more microfilaments, suggestive of more contractile material. However, this cannot be the whole explanation, because newly formed small blood vessels (as in neonatal animals, or in recently healed wounds) do not respond to histamine, despite the presence of large numbers of endothelial microfilaments. Perhaps only venular endothelial cells have the proper receptors, but this also is pure conjecture. A new lead may emerge from recent work in Palade's laboratory: morphologically, the junctions between endothelial cells appear looser in the venules than in the capillaries and arterioles.

Leakage by Direct Vascular Injury

This is easily understood: a burn or a blow will injure any blood vessel within reach, be it an arteriole, a capillary, or a venule. If its wall is actually torn it will simply bleed; however, if the endothelium alone is damaged, but the basement membrane remains more or less intact, then the blood cells will be retained while plasma will seep out – that is, leakage will occur. You can now guess the functional implications of this type of injury in comparison with the histamine-type leaks. Clearly *it will last longer*, up to a day or two, until the vessel is plugged by a thrombus or is repaired.

Experimentally, it is easy to demonstrate these basic

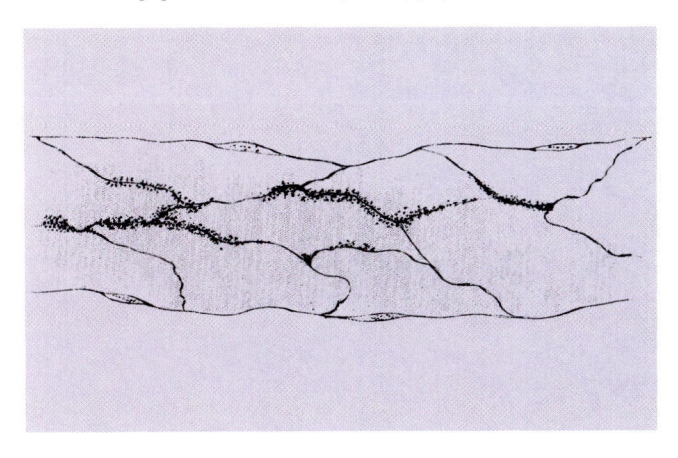

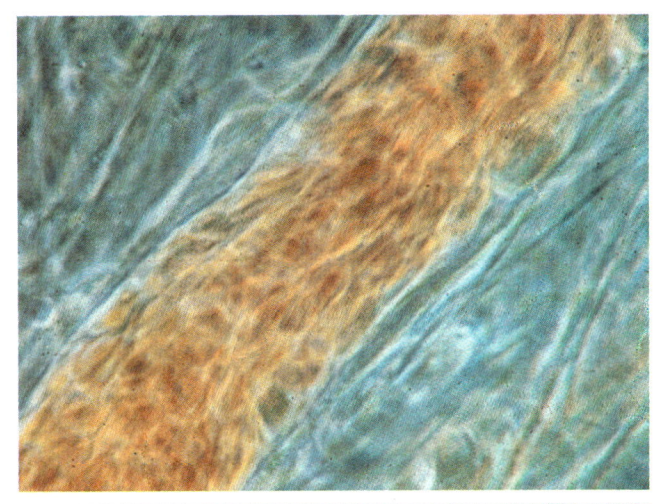

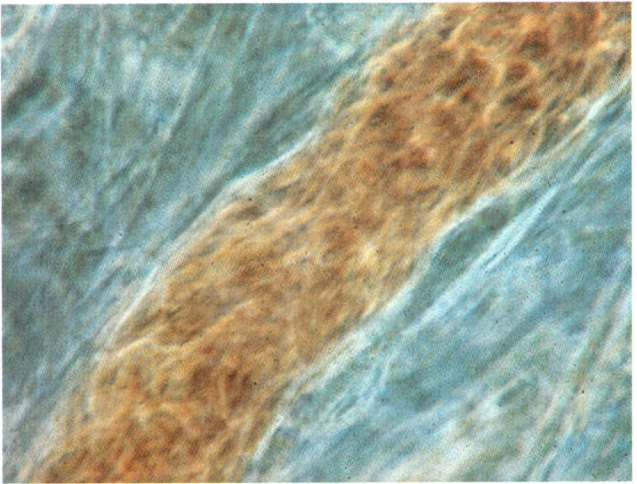

Figure 19. (top) Direct vascular injury after a burn (rat abdominal fascia burned through the skin). Generalized labelling (that is, generalized leakage) of practically the entire microcirculatory network in the subcutaneous tissue.

Figure 20. (middle) Histamine-type vascular labelling (venules only) at the periphery of the burn illustrated in Figure 19.

Figure 21. (bottom) Direct injury of a dermal capillary after a mild burn (the lumen is marked by an *asterisk*). Note endothelial gap (lower left), swollen aspect of endothelium and pericytes, and large amount of protein (including strands of fibrin) retained within the basement membrane. Much protein has also escaped, as proven by the wisps of fibrin in the surroundings, especially at upper right.

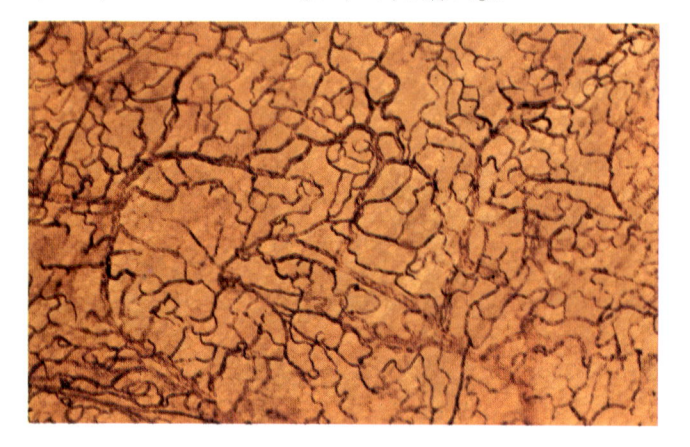

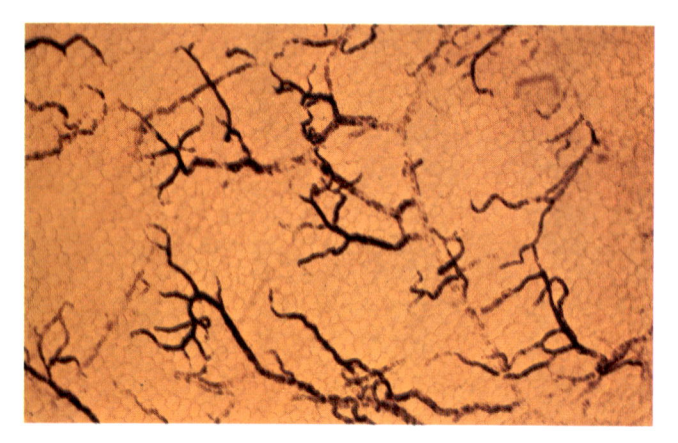

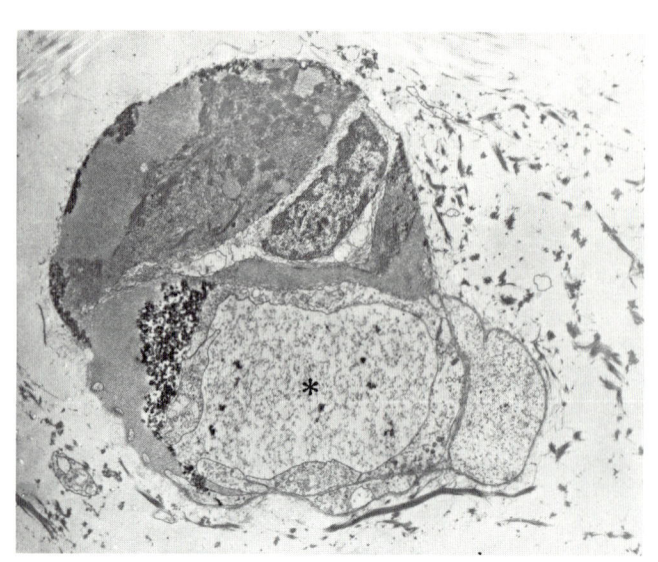

aspects of direct vascular injury. Employing rats that are under prolonged anesthesia with barbiturates, you can produce a small burn on their abdominal skin. Immediately thereafter carbon black is injected intravenously, and half an hour later, when the circulating carbon black is almost completely removed by the littoral phagocytic cells, the rat is sacrificed with an overdose of barbiturates and the abdominal skin is removed. A striking picture appears on the fascia of the abdominal muscles (Figure 19): directly beneath the burned area, the entire microcirculatory network is labelled, including the capillaries; all around you will notice a halo of venular labelling, the result of mediators that have diffused outward from the central area (Figure 20).

The electron microscopic aspect of direct damage is very nonspecific, as you may imagine; one example, a capillary injured by heat, is shown in Figure 21. The ultimate fate of such vessels will vary depending upon the degree of the damage. For the capillary shown in Figure 21, we may surmise that the endothelial cells will die and slough off and that new ones will creep back along the basement membrane (coming from intact vessels), while platelets will have temporarily plugged the gap. The proteins and lipids that accumulated against the basement membrane will be phagocytized and digested, presumably by the endothelium itself and by the pericytes.

Under the heading of direct vascular injury we should also mention a peculiar but common phenomenon that was long thought to represent an entity of its own; it goes under the clumsy name of *delayed-prolonged vascular leakage*. The main characteristics of this phenomenon are as the name implies: *a)* that the oozing starts some time after the application of the injury (the delay being in the order of hours) and *b)* that it lasts significantly longer (several hours) than leakage caused by histamine-type mediators. As you well know, exposure to the sun is fun while it lasts, but the evening can be very uncomfortable. Experimentally, one can produce delayed-prolonged leakage by very mild heat injuries of the skin (such as 54° C for 20 seconds), with cold, with ultraviolet rays, and with certain bacterial toxins. Whatever the agent, *the effect can never be prevented with antihistaminic drugs*, which suggests that histamine is not involved in this kind of leakage. All this raises a number of questions: how can one explain the delay, and the long duration?

It has been suggested that delayed-prolonged leakage might be due to a special mediator (or set of mediators) which would also need time to build up locally. A simpler and perhaps more likely explanation is mild, direct injury to the endothelium. One can easily surmise that endothelial cells, injured by a brief exposure to heat, may remain alive for several hours before they show signs of injury, eventually causing them to retract their margins and perhaps drop off.

Formation of the Exudate: An Overview

Now that we have broken down the phenomenon of vascular leakage into its component parts, we will put it together again and see how the exudate forms in a given case; in a skin burn, for example.

In the center, where the tissue is rapidly killed, the circulation stops and no fluid is lost. All around is a ring-shaped zone where *all* the small vessels are injured (direct injury), but not enough to stop the blood flow. And again around this area is a third zone in which the venules only leak – not because the heat has reached them, but because they are stimulated by histamine-type mediators diffusing from the two central zones. All this starts within seconds of the burn.

In the meantime, the arterioles dilate in and around the injured areas (either by an axon reflex, or because chemical mediators have stimulated their wall). This causes the blood pressure to rise throughout the microcirculatory network. Wherever the endothelium is still intact, this will increase the normal transudation (Figure 22). But wherever there are gaps in the endothelium (caused either by mediators or by direct injury), plasma escapes, the protein concentration in the interstitial fluid rises, and the overall result is therefore an exudate (Figure 23). This process has several consequences: *a)* The amount of protein in the tissue spaces tends to counterbalance the osmotic effect of the protein inside the blood vessels; thus more water will be retained in the tissues, aggravating the effect of the leakage. *b)* The blood in the microcirculation, having lost much of its plasma to the tissues, becomes more viscous. In some places it will be reduced to packed red blood cells, a sort of red sausage that finds it very difficult to wiggle along the vessel. Blood flow may stop, temporarily or even permanently. This is referred to as *stasis*. The viscosity of the blood depends

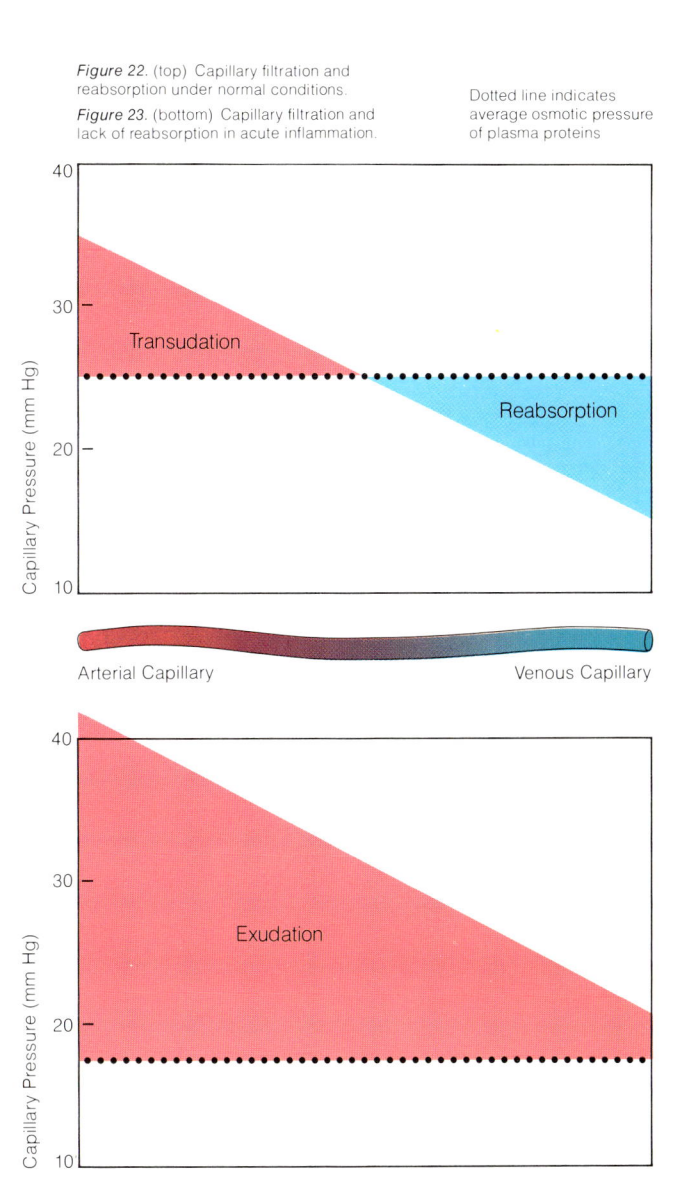

Figure 22. (top) Capillary filtration and reabsorption under normal conditions.
Figure 23. (bottom) Capillary filtration and lack of reabsorption in acute inflammation.
Dotted line indicates average osmotic pressure of plasma proteins

largely on the hematocrit: if the percentage volume of packed red blood cells rises above 60 to 70%, the viscosity rises disproportionately (Figure 24). This will cause an increased resistance to flow, hence an increased pressure upstream, hence an increased loss of fluid – hence a vicious circle.

Common sense will tell you that this local disturbance, entailing a loss of fluid, must be brought under control, or all the plasma could be lost even to a mosquito bite. Foremost in this mechanism of control are the blood platelets, which will rush to plug the endothelial gaps, whatever their nature. Then the arteriolar flare as well as the

Figure 24. (top) With rising hematocrit, the viscosity of the blood rises sharply.

Figure 25. (bottom) Major phases of vascular leakage in inflammation.

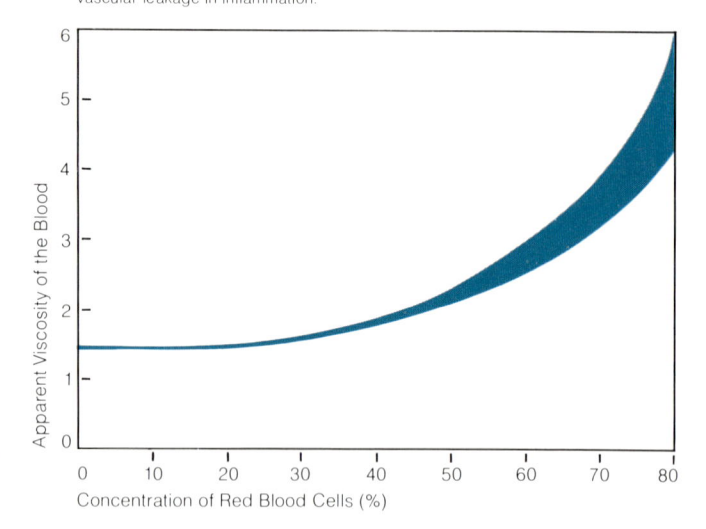

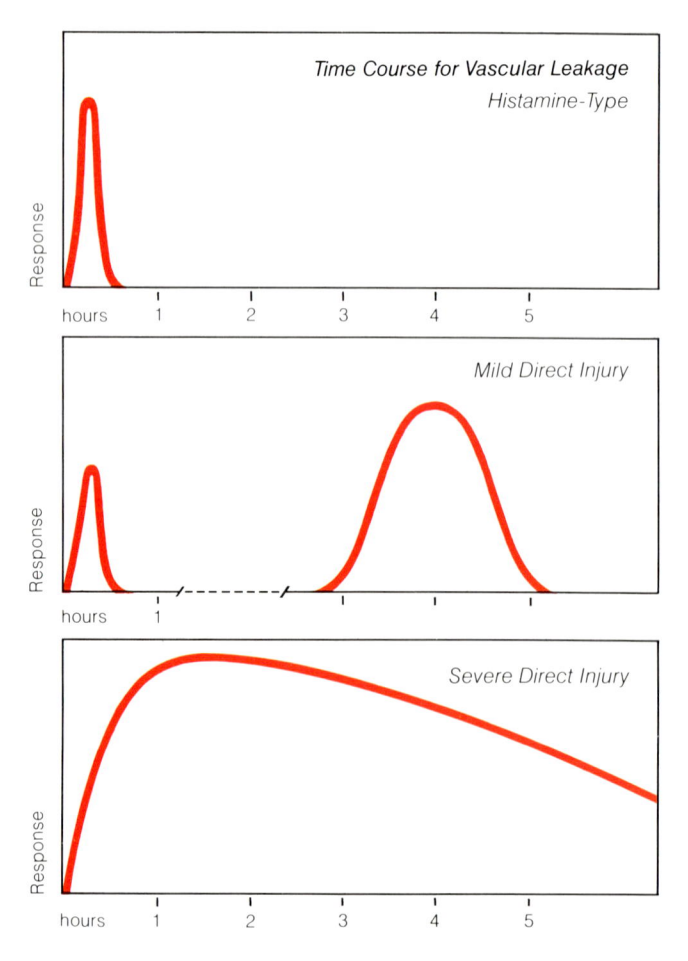

halo of histamine-type leakage will subside (the supply of mediators decreases sharply after the first few hours). Another limit to the local swelling is set by the distensibility of the tissue, which can be measured in terms of tissue pressure. This is normally very low (of the order of 1 to 4 mm Hg). As fluid accumulates in the interstitial spaces, this pressure rises sharply; at some point it will equal the leaking pressure, and the swelling will stop.

Does this also mean that the *leakage* will stop? Not necessarily, because fluid can continue to escape and then drain off through the lymphatics. Lymph flow can rise tremendously as a result of inflammation. For example, in the paw of a normal, anesthetized dog, lymph pressure is so low that it is not measurable; but if the tip of the paw is scalded with boiling water (we never like to read about this experiment) the lymph pressure can rise as high as 120 cm of water. This means that large amounts of exudate will be carried to the local lymph nodes, which promptly enter into action as filters.

You might wonder how the lymphatic vessels contained within the inflammatory focus can remain open to drain the fluid, since they are in a tissue with very high internal pressure. Actually, the lymphatic vessels are kept open by a neat structural arrangement. Many years ago, Pullinger and Florey demonstrated that the lymphatic wall is anchored to the surrounding stroma by loose, thread-like attachments; when the tissues swell, these "tethering lines" become taut and cause the lymphatics to open more widely. Remember also that in the lymphatics the endothelial cells are rather loosely joined and that the basement membrane is very thin and incomplete: both these features help one to understand how even large particles, such as red blood cells, are able to find their way into the lymphatics and reach the lymph nodes.

Let us now summarize the pathogenesis of the exudate (Figure 25). Its fluid portion is contributed in the very beginning by a burst of histamine-type leakage. If the injury is mild (as in a sunburn) the onset of the major phase of leakage may be delayed. If the injury is great (as in a severe burn), massive leakage occurs rapidly, because direct endothelial disruption occurs instantly – virtually an "accelerated" delayed response. And there will always be an admixture of "physiological" transudation, increased by the active hyperemia and by the venous congestion.

Types of Exudate

The gross aspect of the exudate can vary a great deal, because one or another of its components may prevail; thus, in practice, it will be useful to qualify it with an adjective. *Serous* exudate contains few cells, and therefore resembles blood serum; its presence suggests a rather mild type of vascular injury. *But remember that lack of neutrophils may correspond to two entirely opposite conditions — lack of bacterial stimulus (good) or lack of bodily response (bad). Purulent* exudate (pus) implies a large concentration of neutrophils and, therefore, usually the presence of bacteria that attract polymorphs. The concentration of neutrophils is variable: streptococcal infections, for instance, tend to induce rather thin pus; staphylococcal infections induce a heavier leukocytic exudation and the pus is therefore more "creamy," that is, whiter and thicker. *Hemorrhagic* exudate is the consequence of severe capillary damage. *Fibrinous* exudate is seen characteristically on serous surfaces (pericardium, pleura); the whitish layer of fibrin can be several mm in thickness, and on the pericardium the pulsations work it into a velvety surface (Figure 26). The mechanism whereby large amounts of fibrin polymerize on the serous surfaces is not clear. A classic example occurs in terminal uremic patients; this is aseptic (not due to infection), and has not yet been reproduced experimentally.

Effects of the Inflammatory Focus

It is now well established that the inflammatory reaction — although it represents, typically, a reaction to damage — can bring about some local damage of its own. Severe, irreversible stasis can bring about infarction, but the vascular damage resulting in stasis is usually due to the agent itself. The polymorphs can be very destructive; a classic example is the Arthus reaction, in which the walls of the venules are digested by swarms of neutrophils. The enzymatic equipment of these cells includes collagenase as well as elastase, which means that even the toughest components of connective tissue can be broken down.

In a serous cavity the fibrinous exudate can glue together two adjacent surfaces; and if the fibrin is then replaced ("organized") by connective tissue, the apposed surfaces can be permanently joined, forming what is called an *adhesion*.

Figure 26. Fibrinous exudate. Histologic section of epicardium covered with pink masses of fibrin (uremic pericarditis).

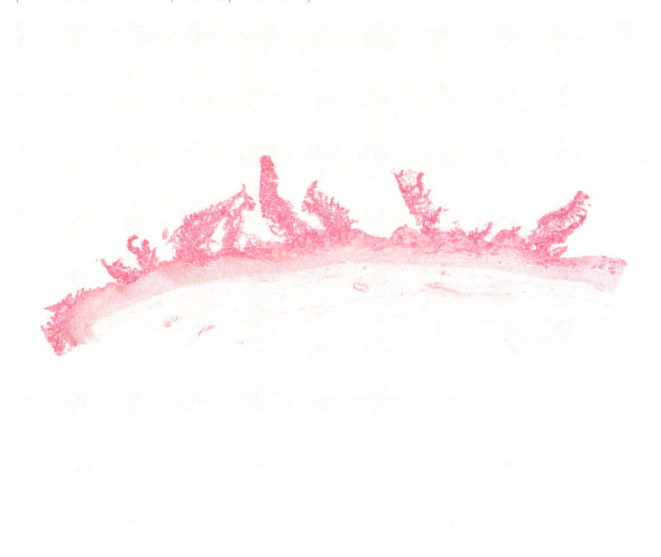

The exudate and products of tissue breakdown will drain toward the lymph nodes. If pathogenic bacteria are included, they may create an additional problem even while they are being drained away. Sometimes they seep out of the wall of the lymphatic vessel (which, as we have seen, is easy to cross — inward as well as outward) and set up an inflammatory reaction all along the course of the vessel. The reaction may become clinically visible as a red streak, usually originating from an obvious focus of infection — this is called *lymphangitis*. When the pathologic material reaches the lymph node, it does not necessarily set up another inflammatory reaction. In the simplest case it will be phagocytized by the cells that line the sinuses. These phagocytic cells can also be stimulated to undergo hyperplasia. If antigens are involved, an immune response may be initiated. If the irritation is severe, a *lymphadenitis* will develop: clinically, the node will become swollen and tender.

Not all the pathologic products of the inflammatory focus will be filtered out by the lymph nodes. Part of these products will escape phagocytosis and thereby reach the bloodstream indirectly. Another part will be reabsorbed directly by the local blood capillaries and venules. In this manner an inflammatory focus may make its presence felt throughout the body, and may cause fever, leukocytosis, and an increase in the erythrocyte sedimentation rate (see Systemic Effects of Inflammation).

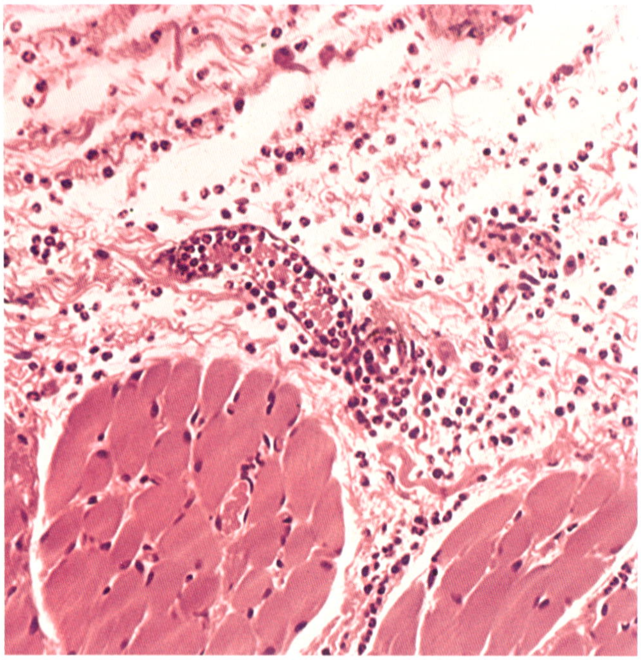

Figure 27. Acute inflammatory infiltrate (muscular fascia). Note venule nearly filled with leukocytes (H & E stain).

Leukocytic Infiltration

When we look at a piece of inflamed tissue under a microscope, the most striking and characteristic thing we see – the "pathognomonic" feature – is the presence of leukocytes (Figures 27, 28). These cells come from the blood; they first stick to the walls of the blood vessels, then emigrate outward into the tissues (Figures 29-31), and crawl towards whatever might have provoked the inflammatory response – perhaps a clump of bacteria, or perhaps a group of damaged cells. This process of directional locomotion is called *chemotaxis*. The leukocytes then do their best to eat up and digest the offending agent – *phagocytosis*.

Leukocytic Sticking

In animals without blood vessels, mobile mesodermal cells accumulate at sites of injury or around bits of foreign material. These mobile cells are analogous to mammalian leukocytes, except that the latter are enclosed within the bloodstream. The first step in getting mammalian leukocytes out into the tissues where they are needed (in an inflammatory response) is to have them stick to the vessel walls in the appropriate area. This is obviously a crucial event in inflammation, but we know remarkably little about how it occurs. It does not seem to be a nonspecific result of increased vascular permeability. If histamine is injected into the skin, the leukocytic infiltration is slight. On the other hand, if bacteria are present or if there is tissue damage, then we see massive sticking (and emigration) of leukocytes. Probably the bacteria and the damaged tissue liberate factors that somehow alter the endothelial lining of the blood vessels so that it becomes sticky for leukocytes. Cohnheim envisaged "a molecular change in the vessel walls," but its nature remains a mystery.

It was once thought that a "glue" forms on the luminal surfaces of the endothelial cells, particularly in the venules, where most of the sticking occurs. Using special staining techniques (ruthenium red, colloidal iron), electron microscopy has revealed the presence of an amorphous "cell coat" material on the endothelial surface of normal blood vessels. But, somewhat disappointingly, there does not seem to be any change in this layer in inflammation; at least there is no alteration that can be detected morphologically. Another idea is that the attachment is due to the formation of ionic bridges, eg, with Ca^{++}, between the leukocyte and the endothelial cell sur-

Figure 28. Scanning electron micrograph (SEM) showing leukocytes in inflamed tissue.

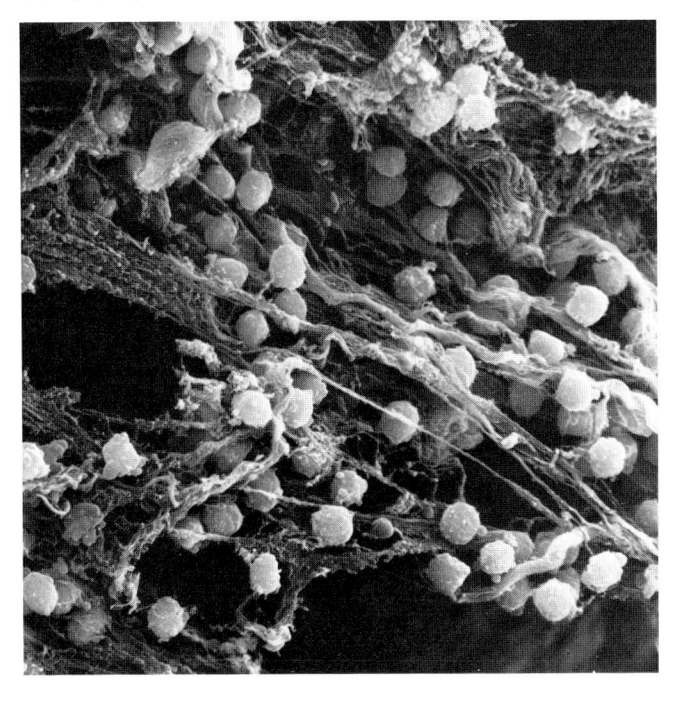

Figure 29. Leukocytes stuck to the wall of a venule in an inflamed tissue (SEM).

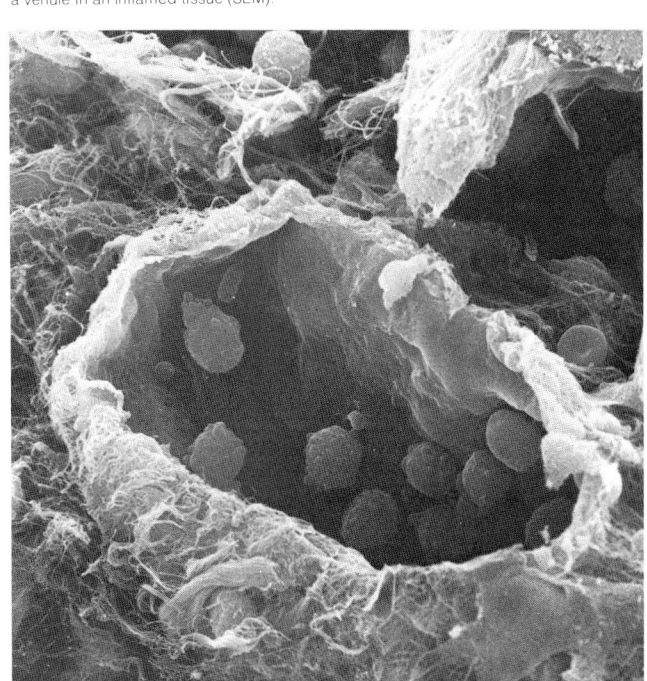

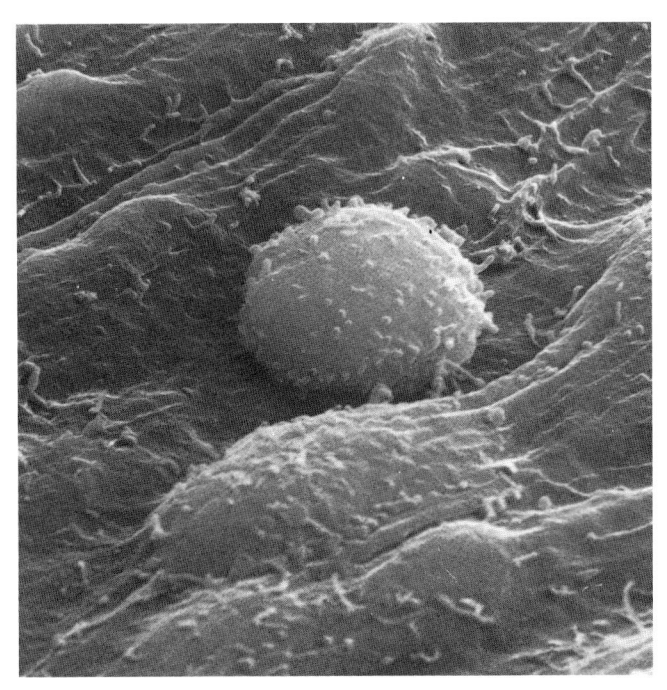

Figure 30. A leukocyte stuck to a venular wall and probably preparing to crawl through it (see Figure 31) to reach the tissue (SEM).

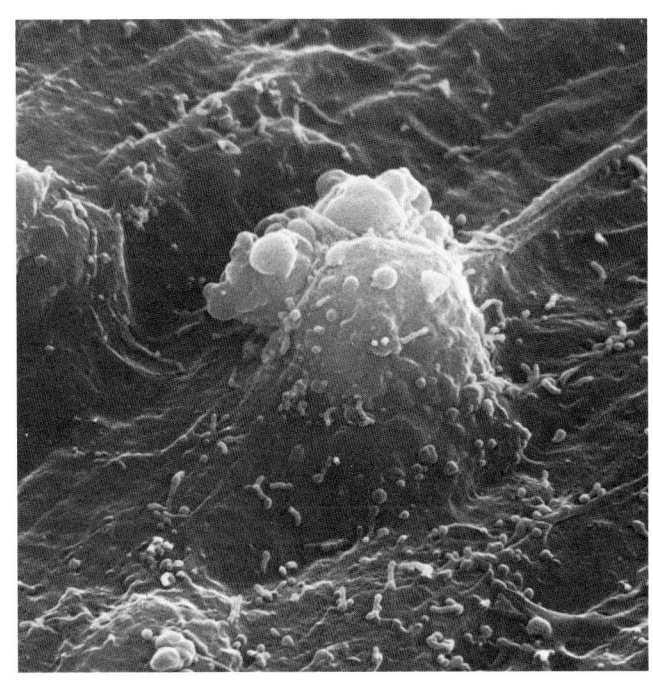

Figure 31. A leukocyte crawling through a venular wall (SEM).

Figure 32. Schema of diapedesis of leukocytes.

- Margination of leukocyte (to periphery of blood stream) — Direction of blood flow; Plasmatic Zone (free of erythrocytes)
- Sticking of leukocyte to endothelium (pavementing) — Endothelium
- Movement of leukocyte over endothelial surface — Junction
- Leukocyte finds interendothelial junction — Erythrocytes
- Diapedesis (emigration) (via junction) — Basement Membrane
- Leukocyte leaves vessel
- Locomotion of leukocyte in tissues — Tissue

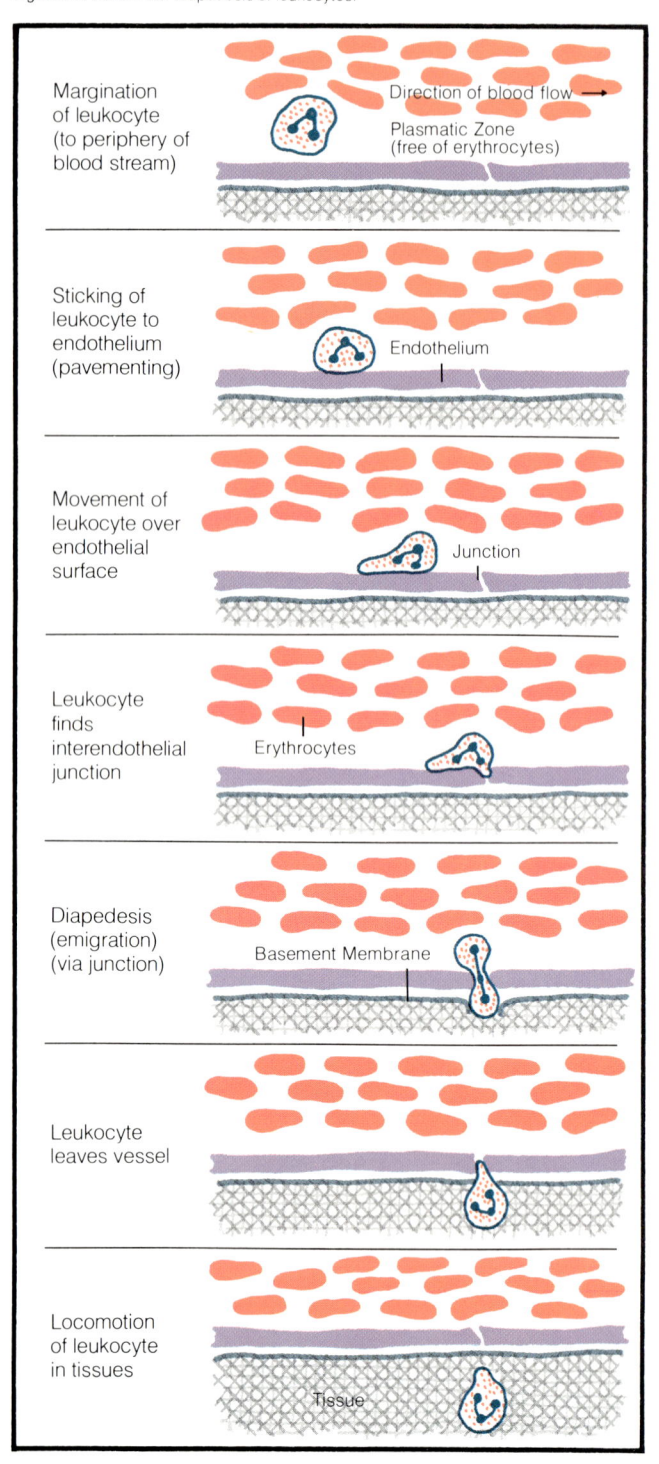

face. However, both the leukocyte and the endothelial cell are negatively charged, so it is difficult to see how they could get close enough to form such bridges. It is possible that inflammation induces an appropriate change in the endothelial surface (perhaps a change in charge) that allows closer cell-to-cell contact, but this is obviously a difficult concept to test. However, there seems little doubt that divalent ions such as Ca^{++} play a part in the process. This has been shown in experiments in which sticking was inhibited in animals treated with EDTA (ethylenediaminotetraacetate), a chelating agent that removes free calcium ions from the blood. This inhibition was shown by direct observation of inflamed blood vessels in the rabbit ear chamber, in the cheek pouch of the hamster, and in the mouse mesentery. Local anesthetic drugs also inhibit leukocytic sticking in experimental animals; the mechanism is obscure, but it is known that such agents can displace Ca^{++} from binding sites in membranes.

Leukocytic Emigration (Diapedesis)

In acute inflammation, diapedesis of leukocytes across the venular wall occurs via the interendothelial junctions (Figure 32). This fact was recorded in the drawings of Arnold in 1875 (Figure 33), and was confirmed by electron microscopy, more than a century later, by Vincent Marchesi and Sir Howard (later Lord) Florey at Oxford. We can see this process in Figures 34-36. Individual leukocytes usually take from 2 to 12 minutes to get completely across the vessel wall.

Perhaps some of the leukocytes sneak out through gaps prepared for them by histamine-type mediators (this is not well established). However, it is certain that they do not *need* such preformed gaps, because it is possible to produce diapedesis without an accompanying increase in permeability. Nor does diapedesis cause vascular leakage, which shows how tightly the leukocytes must squeeze themselves between the endothelial cells. Here is the experiment: in the rat, a subcutaneous injection of serum produces a lively inflammatory response (with the rapid onset of increased vascular permeability). Four hours later, vascular leakage has subsided, whereas diapedesis is at its peak. India ink, injected intravenously at this stage, does not cause "carbon labelling" of the vessels because the endothelium closes up immediately behind the emigrating leukocytes.

Figure 33. Leukocytes emigrating from a small inflamed vessel in frog mesentery, as observed by Julius Arnold and reported in *Virchow's Archiv für pathologische Anatomie* (1875).

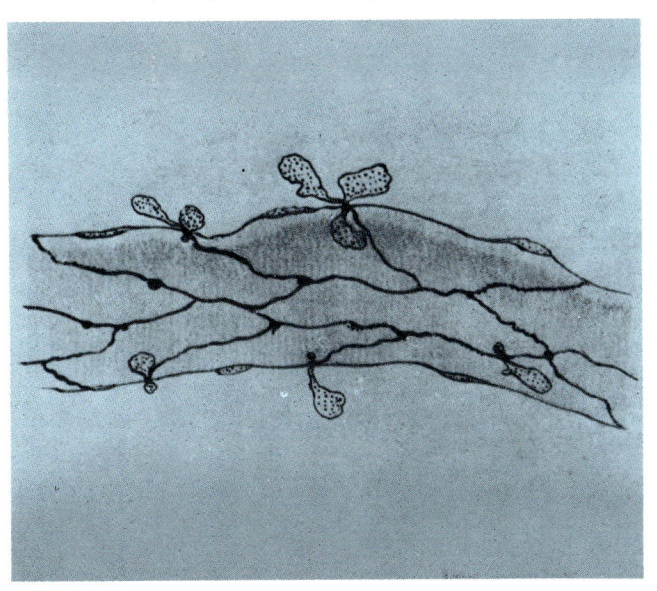

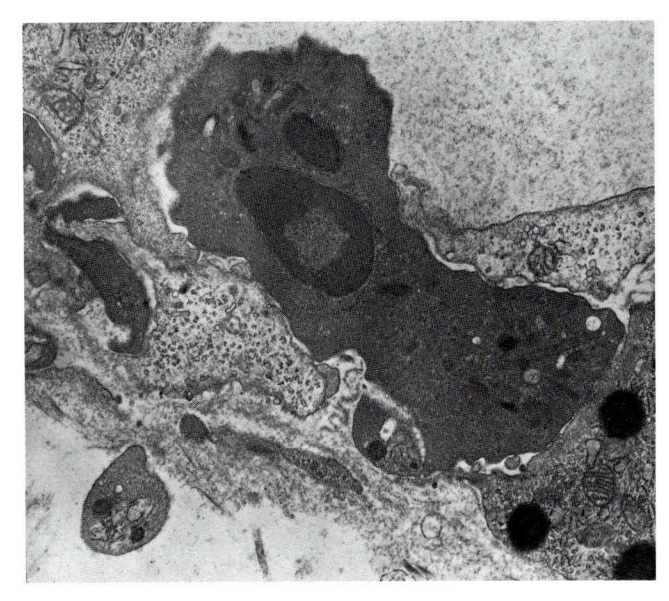

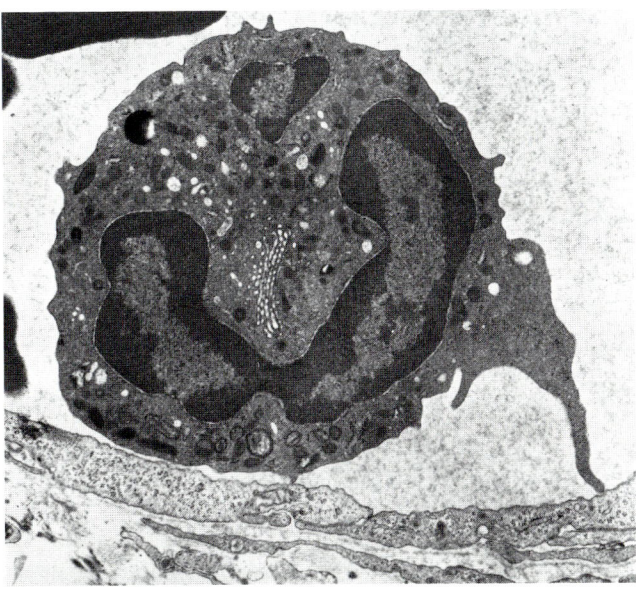

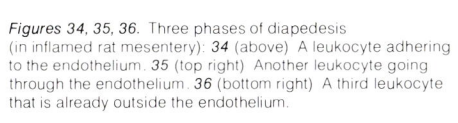

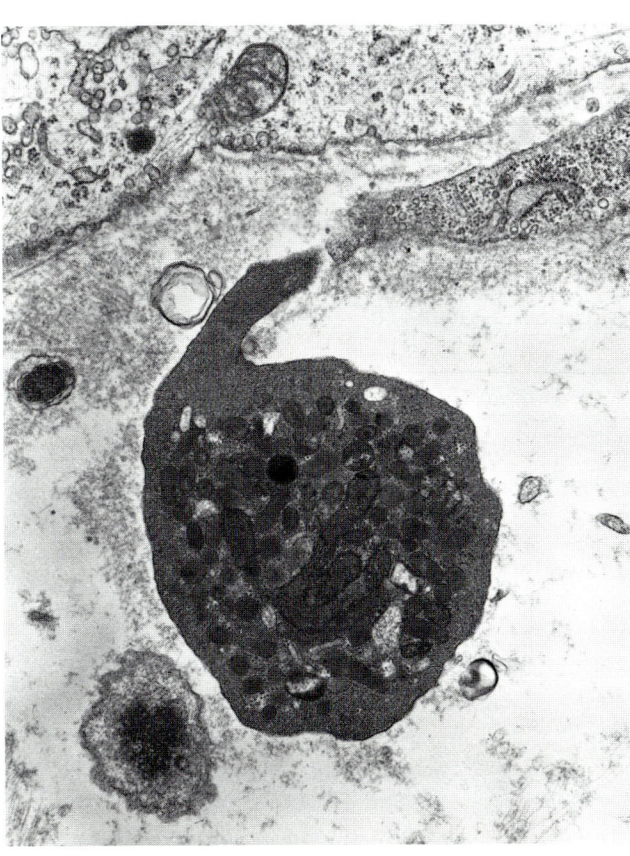

Figures 34, 35, 36. Three phases of diapedesis (in inflamed rat mesentery): *34* (above) A leukocyte adhering to the endothelium. *35* (top right) Another leukocyte going through the endothelium. *36* (bottom right) A third leukocyte that is already outside the endothelium.

Figure 37. Histologic section of gonococcal pus: mostly polymorphs, cell debris, and a few erythrocytes.

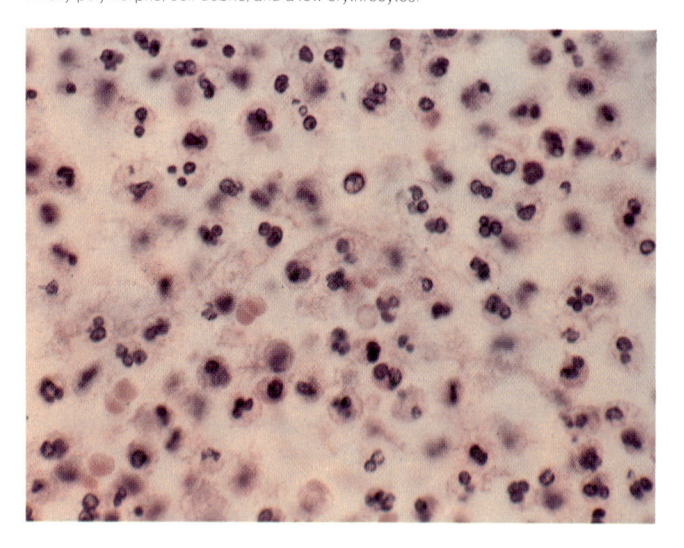

Although the emigrating leukocytes may not cause leaks in the endothelium, they temporarily tear apart the basement membrane around the vessel. They probably have no alternative. A simple experiment devised by John Hurley to prove this point is to cause vascular labelling by injecting India ink intravenously immediately after injecting histamine into the skin. If this area of skin already shows active diapedesis (for example, in response to an injection of serum four hours earlier), the labelled venules spill their carbon out into the tissue spaces through holes punched in the basement membrane by the escaping leukocytes.

We do not know what stimulates the leukocytes to emigrate. It is possible that chemotactic agents released in the tissues might seep into the junctions and attract the pavemented leukocytes out of the vessel, but there is no evidence to support this theory, nor do we know how the leukocyte traverses the basement membrane — whether by pure mechanical force, by enzymatic lysis, or by some other process.

Before leaving this topic, let us mention a minor controversy concerning another sort of leukocytic emigration. It has been claimed that lymphocytes cross venular walls in lymph nodes by passing through the cytoplasm of the endothelial cells. However, in more recent studies using careful serial sectioning techniques, Gutta Schoefl demonstrated that, here too, emigration occurs through the junctions.

What Kinds of Leukocytes Emigrate in Acute Inflammation – and When?

In the early stages of the acute inflammatory response, the predominant cell infiltrating the tissues is the *neutrophil polymorphonuclear leukocyte*. After a day or so, as the intensity of the response subsides, the predominant cell is the *mononuclear phagocyte* (usually called a *macrophage* when found in the tissues); this cell is derived from the blood monocyte.

If the tissue is infected with pyogenic (pus-producing) bacteria, the influx of neutrophils is greatly enhanced and sustained. If the bacteria survive long enough they can provoke the formation of *abscesses*. These are *newly formed cavities that contain pus*. Pus consists of myriads of neutrophils in various stages of degeneration, floating in exudate fluid (Figure 37).

The time sequence for leukocytic emigration has been worked out experimentally by collecting and counting exudate cells at various times after injecting phlogistic agents (an old-fashioned term for inflammatory agents) into the pleural or peritoneal cavity of rats. A typical experiment is shown in Figure 38; this depicts the numbers of neutrophils and mononuclear phagocytes found in the pleural cavity of rats sacrificed at various times after injecting rat serum. Clearly, the peak polymorph emigration occurs within the first 6 hours, whereas the peak mononuclear phagocyte emigration is delayed another 6 hours or so. The mononuclear cells predominate after 12 hours, and by 48 hours they are virtually the only cells found in the exudate. In striking contrast is the pattern seen after the injection of living *Klebsiella pneumoniae* organisms into the pleural cavity of rats (Figure 39). In this situation, enormous numbers of neutrophils continually pour into the cavity while mononuclear emigration remains relatively insignificant.

It is not understood why the major infiltration of mononuclear phagocytes occurs after the neutrophil peak. Some investigators have attributed it to a combination of two factors: first, the locomotion of the macrophages is relatively sluggish, and secondly, macrophages can live for days or months, whereas neutrophils only last for a matter of hours after emigration. This hypothesis may be a partial explanation for the findings, at least for the precipitous fall in neutrophil numbers after the peak is reached compared with the much slower decline in

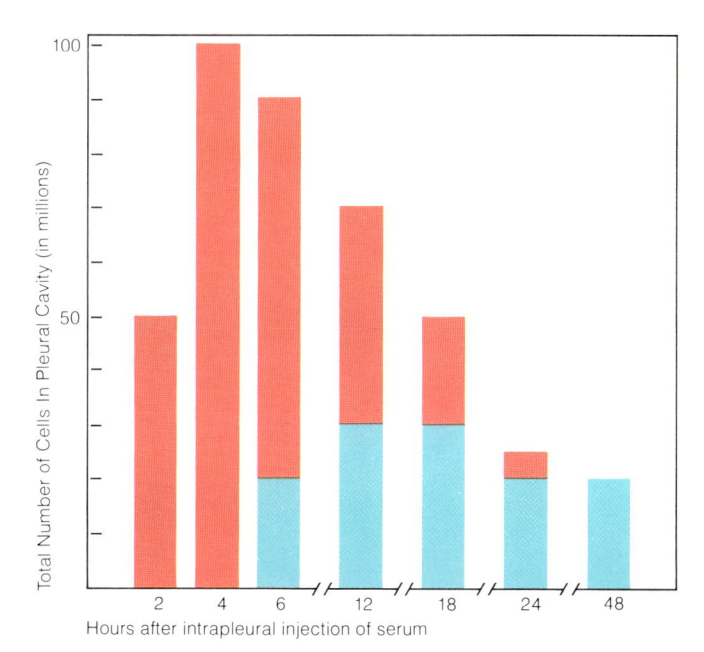

Figure 38. (below left) Graph showing numbers of neutrophils and mononuclear phagocytes entering an inflamed area at various intervals (following an injection of serum into rat pleural cavity).

Figure 39. (below) Graph showing continued influx of neutrophils following an intrapleural injection of living *Klebsiella pneumoniae* organisms into a rat pleural cavity.

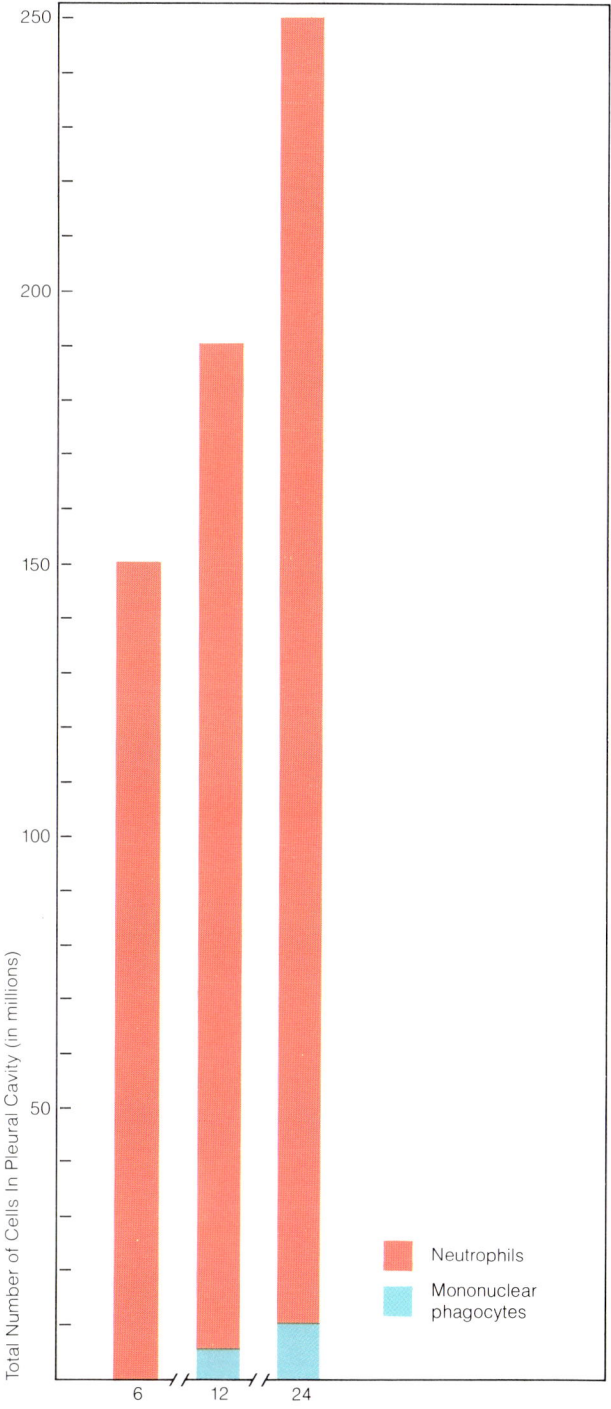

numbers of mononuclear cells. However, from experiments such as those shown in Figure 38, it is apparent that proportionally more neutrophils emigrate into the inflammatory focus in the early stages, whereas more monocytes enter the lesion later. This biphasic response could result from the sequential action of specific chemical mediators. In other words, there may be a mediator that causes neutrophil emigration, followed by a mediator that causes monocyte emigration. In recent years, it has been demonstrated that certain chemotactic agents may specifically attract certain kinds of leukocytes. In the present context, the most relevant of these specific agents is one described as a monocyte chemotactic factor released from neutrophils.

Chemotaxis

Chemotaxis — the attraction of cells towards chemical substances — is a subject that has fascinated biologists for nearly 100 years. The term was originally used by Pfeffer in 1884 to describe the attraction of spermatozoids of certain ferns toward malic acid. In 1888, Leber was the first to observe chemotactically directed movement of leukocytes. He injected guinea pig corneas with molds or with products of putrefied rabbit muscle and then, after waiting for several hours until the corneas were in-

Figure 40. Dark field micrographs showing the tracks produced by human neutrophils crawling on a slide (single 15-minute exposure of photographic frame) *Top:* cells crawling at random, in relation to a piece of fibrin (right); *Bottom:* cells crawling towards a clump of living *Staphylococcus epidermidis* organisms (right) — chemotactic locomotion.

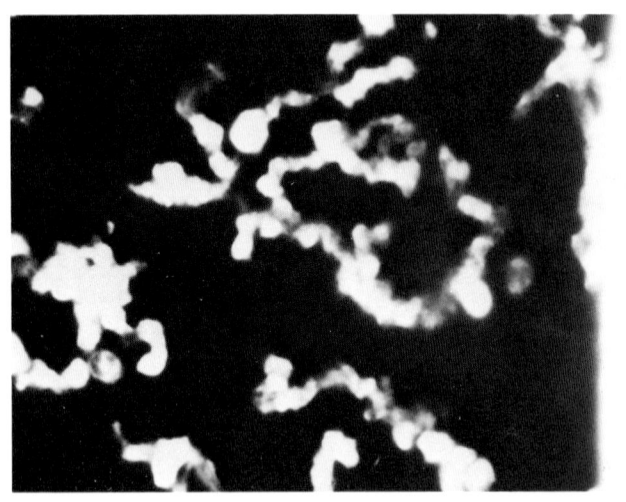

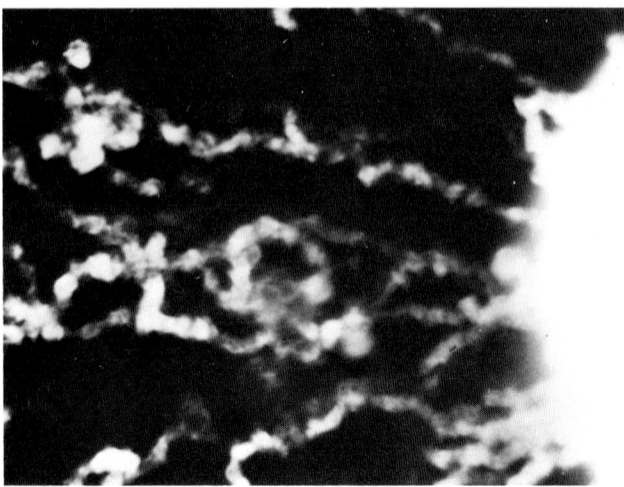

filtrated with leukocytes, he removed the corneas and examined them under the microscope. He observed the leukocytes moving directly towards the injection sites. Over the next 50 years, chemotaxis was studied by many workers using a wide variety of methods. By the 1940s it was generally believed that neutrophils were attracted by bacteria and their products, as well as by factors released during tissue breakdown.

However, at Oxford in the early 1950s, Henry Harris proposed that much of the data concerning leukocyte chemotaxis were obtained from experiments that were badly controlled. He attacked the common assumption that accumulation of leukocytes at a particular site necessarily meant that the cells had been attracted there chemotactically. He pointed out that such a finding could just as easily be explained by a local, nonspecific trapping of randomly moving cells. Harris particularly stressed that chemotaxis can only be assessed if directional locomotion of the cells is directly observed or recorded. He devised a simple but elegant system in which neutrophils were incorporated into a film of clotted plasma between a slide and a coverslip. Using dark field microscopy (in which cells show up as white blobs on a black background), the paths traced by the cells could be recorded by making long exposures of a single photographic frame (Figure 40). Using this technique, Harris confirmed that clumps of various bacteria were chemotactic but found no polarization of the tracks towards fragments of injured or autolysed tissue (we shall reexamine this result in a moment).

The next important development occurred in Australia in 1962, when Stephen Boyden introduced a new assay system for chemotaxis. This system consists essentially of a chamber with two compartments separated by a horizontal filter membrane (Figure 41). Leukocytes placed in the upper compartment crawl through the pores of the filter (Figure 41) when a chemotactic solution is placed in the lower compartment. The chemotactic activity of the fluid in the lower compartment is evaluated by counting the number of cells on the lower side of the filter (or the extent of penetration of cells into the filter) at the end of a certain period of time.

As a technique, Boyden's system has enjoyed wide popularity. It is simple, it can be conveniently used to assess the chemotactic activity of substances in solution, and it allows some degree of quantitative comparison of different test substances. However, it has been recognized recently that, as ordinarily used, the system may not distinguish between accelerated random locomotion of cells and true chemotaxis. Thus, the test substance may simply stimulate the cells to crawl around faster, and this would result in larger numbers of cells reaching further into the filter, independent of specific chemotactically directed locomotion. Boyden also recognized this problem and performed control experiments in which the chemotactically active solution was placed with the cells in the upper compartment of the chamber. In such cases, the cells showed less tendency to crawl into the

Figure 41. The Boyden chemotactic system.
Leukocytes are placed in the top compartment of the chamber and crawl into a porous filter towards the target solution in the bottom compartment. Cells are counted either on the bottom of the filter or in the filter itself *(x cells per high power field).*

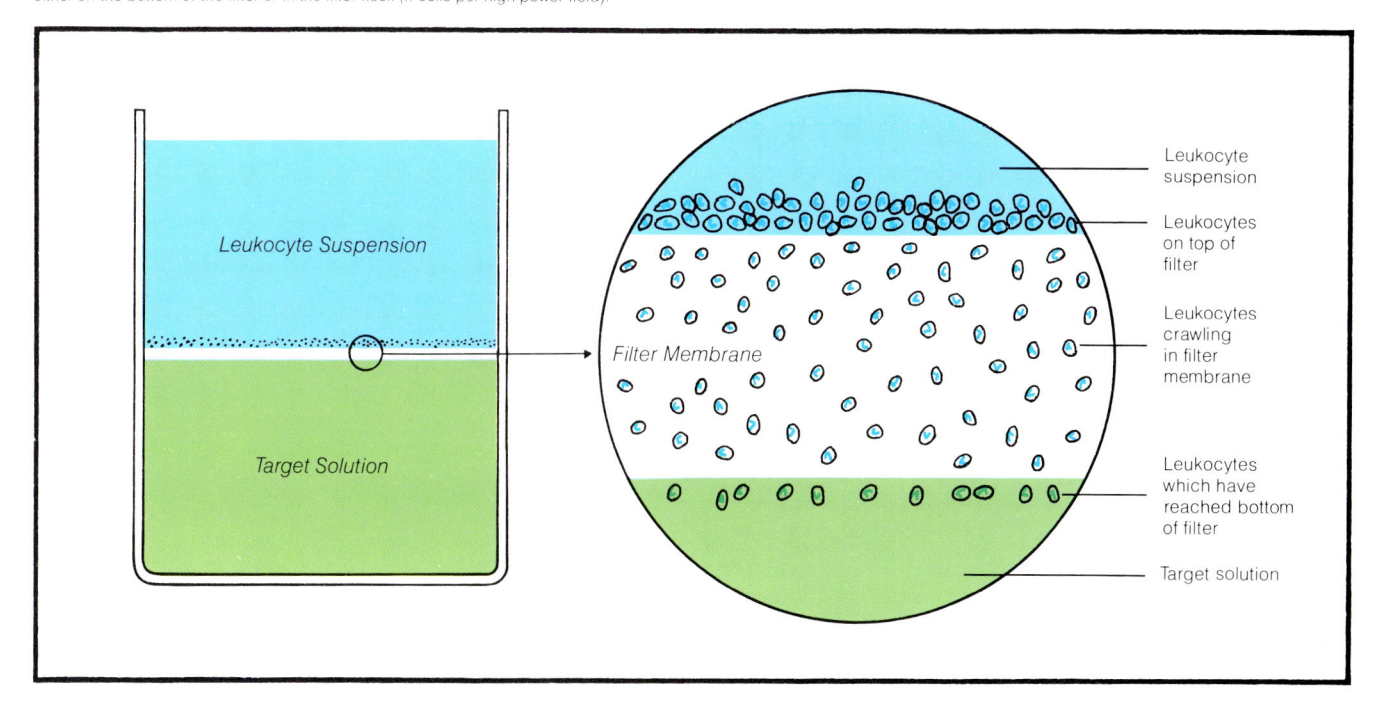

filter than if the solution were placed only in the lower compartment. This was interpreted as evidence that accelerated random locomotion was not involved in a positive result. Recently, however, it has been shown by Sally Zigmond and James Hirsch that a given substance may stimulate random locomotion at low concentrations (such as might develop with slow diffusion of molecules through the filter), but may actually inhibit locomotion at higher concentrations (such as when the test solution is placed directly with the cells in the upper compartment). Because of this problem, Hirsch has urged that data obtained with such indirect techniques as the Boyden system should be checked by direct microscopic observation of leukocytes crawling in thin preparations (such as in the slide-coverslip system used by Harris).

Now that we have described and evaluated the technique, let us return to Boyden's original observations. They are most interesting. He discovered that chemotactic activity (for neutrophils) was generated if serum was incubated with antigen-antibody precipitates. He proposed that such precipitates interact with the serum complement system to liberate chemotactic factors. John Hurley soon adopted the same technique to show that serum incubated with minced tissues also became chemotactic. Ryan and Hurley then used Harris' slide-coverslip technique to directly demonstrate that neutrophils crawled towards tissue fragments that had been previously incubated with fresh serum. These findings not only reinstated the view that chemotactic factors can be released during tissue damage, but also established a new concept: *chemotactic factors can be derived from an interaction between tissue products and serum substrates.* Later, in the section on Mediators, we discuss how this work has been extended, pinpointing the key role of serum complement components in the production of endogenous chemotactic factors, such as C3 fragments and C5 fragments.

There is also evidence that serum-independent chemotactic factors can be released from certain cells. For example, damaged or phagocytizing neutrophils probably release chemotactic molecules – rather like ants releasing "alarm pheromones," thereby calling their colleagues to help them attack a foreign insect invader. From studies of blood cells in slide-coverslip preparations, Marcel Bessis gives the following colorful description of such a process – he calls it "necrotaxis."

Figure 42. A human neutrophil crawling across a glass surface, from left to right (SEM).

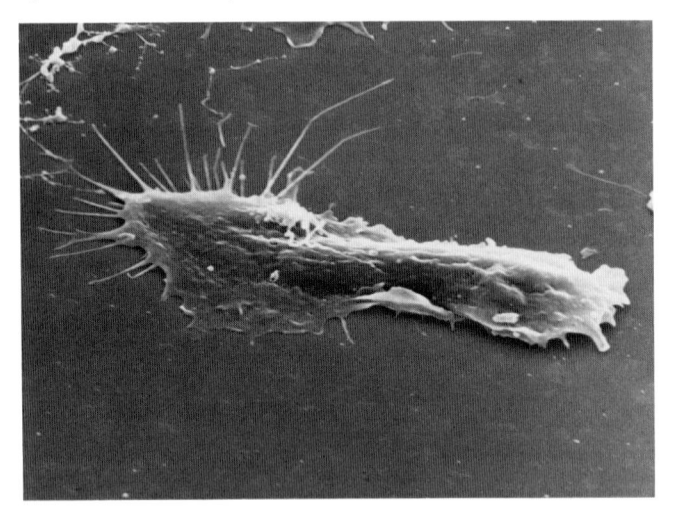

"*On a cellular level, the phenomenon calls to mind large sharks swimming without paying attention to each other, to fasten upon one of their number which has blood escaping from a wound. It can sometimes be observed that after ingesting part of a dead cell, leukocytes abandon a piece of the corpse; this piece does not attract another cell, even if it is near to it.*"

Bessis makes the point here that such chemotactic factors are only released while the cell is in the process of dying and not at later stages.

Mechanisms Involved in Leukocyte Chemotaxis

First, how does the cell detect a gradient of chemotactic molecules so that it knows which way to crawl? Secondly, how does sensing of the gradient actually cause the cell to crawl in the right direction? These are challenging questions of broad biologic interest. It is likely that attractants are detected primarily by specific chemoreceptors on the surface of cells. This certainly seems to be true for bacterial cells that respond chemotactically (*Escherichia coli* has receptors for galactose, glucose, ribose, aspartate and serine). A gradient could be detected by a) a "temporal" mechanism whereby the cell "sniffs the air" (available chemotactic molecules bind to the surface receptor sites) at separate time intervals, or b) a "spatial" mechanism whereby the cell compares the concentration of the attractant at two or more separate locations on its surface at the same time. For bacteria, it seems that a temporal mechanism is involved (implying that individual cells can possess some sort of "memory" system) because sudden decreases in attractant concentrations cause *Salmonella typhimurium* organisms to show uncoordinated tumbling, whereas sudden increases in concentration induce smoother, "super-coordinated," straight-line motion for several minutes. This behavior could result in a directional response along a gradient. On the other hand, the available evidence suggests that a spatial mechanism is more likely to be involved in leukocyte chemotaxis. Sally Zigmond has shown in slide-coverslip preparations that stationary neutrophils exposed to a chemotactic gradient make their first movement towards the chemotactic source, indicating that a leukocyte can sense a difference in the number of chemotactic molecules across its own dimensions – no mean feat! However, we are still far from understanding how sensing of such a gradient can lead to directional movement: in other words, how the actin-myosin contractile machinery of the leukocyte is triggered and coordinated to produce the appropriate response (Figure 42).

The literature is full of studies claiming that chemotaxis (in the Boyden system) is inhibited or enhanced with one treatment or another. For instance, inhibition has been reported with drugs that increase intracellular cyclic AMP. However, it is likely that most of these results are due to inhibition or enhancement of cellular motility and not true effects on chemotactic responsiveness.

Years ago, it was thought that leukocytes were repelled by certain materials, eg, kaolin. This was called *negative chemotaxis*. The evidence for this phenomenon, however, was always rather weak and has not been confirmed in more recent studies.

Chemotaxis *In Vivo*

In rabbit ear chambers, early experiments demonstrated that leukocytes wandered about randomly in injured areas. This was interpreted to mean that chemotaxis was simply an *in vitro* curiosity. This pessimistic view was challenged by Ian Buckley, who proposed that random motility in such studies occurred because the injury was too widespread to allow gradients to develop within the field of the chamber. To examine the point more precisely, Buckley induced a very small focus of heat injury in an ear chamber. He then observed that neutrophils emigrated from the surrounding blood vessels and then crawled directly towards the site of injury.

Phagocytosis

Neutrophils and mononuclear phagocytes enter inflammatory foci with the express purpose of ingesting and disposing of unwanted particulate material, such as bacteria or broken-down cells. This process of *phagocytosis*, or "cellular eating," was discovered by Metchnikoff in 1882. Here is his description (written in 1908) of how he conceived "the phagocytic theory":

"Thus it was in Messina that the great event of my scientific life took place. A zoologist till then, I suddenly became a pathologist. I entered into a new road in which my later activity was to be exerted.

"One day when the whole family had gone to a circus to see some extraordinary performing apes, I remained alone with my microscope, observing the life in the mobile cells of a transparent star-fish larva, when a new thought suddenly flashed across my brain. It struck me that similar cells might serve in the defense of the organism against intruders. Feeling that there was in this something of surpassing interest, I felt so excited that I began striding up and down the room and even went to the seashore to collect my thoughts.

"I said to myself, if my supposition was true, a splinter introduced into the body of a star-fish larva, devoid of blood-vessels or of a nervous system, should soon be surrounded by mobile cells as is to be observed in a man who runs a splinter into his finger. This was no sooner said than done.

"There was a small garden to our dwelling...I fetched from it a few rose thorns and introduced them at once under the skin of some beautiful star-fish larvae as transparent as water.

"I was too excited to sleep that night in the expectation of the result of my experiment, and very early the next morning I ascertained that it had fully succeeded (Figure 43). That experiment formed the basis of the phagocyte theory, to the development of which I devoted the next twenty-five years of my life."

The discovery convinced Metchnikoff that inflammation is a curative response, the essence of which is the reaction by the phagocytes against foreign intruders. At the time, this view ran counter to the common belief that leukocytes actually helped to spread infection rather than contain it. However, he met with the bitterest opposition from proponents of the humoral hypothesis of host protection, which attributed bacterial killing solely to the effects of substances present in the plasma. Eventually, however, it was realized that collaboration was required between humoral factors and phagocytes. Sir Almroth Wright found that phagocytosis of bacteria by leukocytes usually required the presence of serum. He proposed that the bacteria needed to be coated by certain serum factors, called *opsonins*, before phagocytosis could occur.

Figure 43. Larva of *Astropecten* (modified from Metchnikoff by Adami). *(1):* mass of phagocytes (forming a plasmodium *pl*) around thorn; *mes*, mesodermal wandering cells; *ect*, ectoderm; *end*, endoderm. *(2):* high power view of plasmodium; *f*, foreign spicule, *nucl*, nuclei.

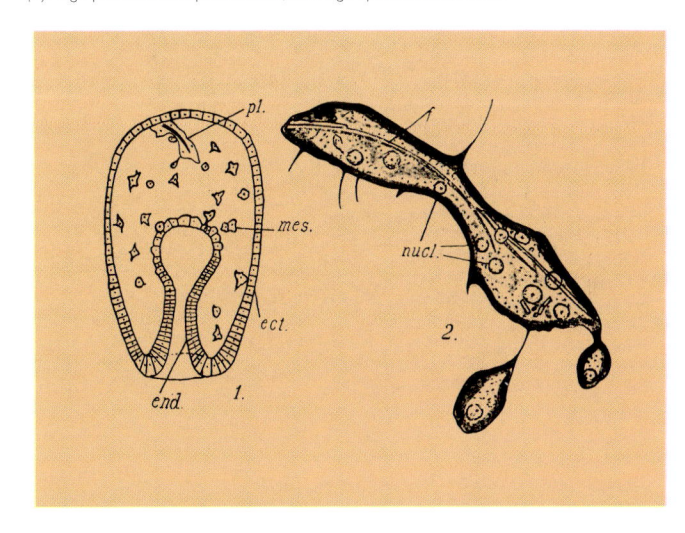

In 1906, George Bernard Shaw wrote *The Doctor's Dilemma*:

"Sir Patrick Cullen: *Opsonin? What the devil is opsonin?*

"Sir Colenso Ridgeon *(an alias for Sir Almroth Wright): Opsonin is what you butter the disease germs with to make your white blood corpuscles eat them...The phagocytes won't eat the microbes unless the microbes are nicely buttered for them. Well, the patient manufactures the butter for himself all right; but my discovery is that the manufacture of that butter, which I call opsonin, goes on in the system by ups and downs...*

"Sir Ralph Bloomfield Bonington: *There is at bottom only one genuinely scientific treatment for all diseases, and that is to stimulate the phagocytes...Find the germ of the disease; prepare from it a suitable anti-toxin; inject it three times a day quarter of an hour before meals; and what is your result? The phagocytes are stimulated; they devour the disease; and the patient recovers – unless, of course, he's too far gone."*

Before dealing with the mechanics of phagocytosis, let us first consider some pertinent characteristics of neutrophils and mononuclear phagocytes – the professional phagocytes.

Neutrophils possess large numbers of cytoplasmic granules. These appear to be of two main types (Figure 44): a) *azurophil granules* (also called *primary* granules because they appear first in cellular development). These are large, dense granules that contain various lysosomal

Figure 44. (top) Neutrophil granules and their contents.
Figure 45. (bottom) The mononuclear phagocyte system (traditionally known as the "Reticuloendothelial system").

Neutrophil Granules and Their Contents

Azurophil (primary) — *large, dense:*
lysosomal enzymes
peroxidase ("myeloperoxidase")
lysozyme (33%)
cationic proteins

Specific (secondary) — *smaller, less dense:*
alkaline phosphatase
lysozyme (67%)
lactoferrin

The Mononuclear Phagocyte System
(The "Reticulo-Endothelial System")

Bone marrow	promonocytes
Blood	monocytes
Tissues	macrophages:
	connective tissue ("histiocytes")
	liver (Kupffer cells)
	lung (alveolar macrophages)
	lymphoid tissues
	(free and fixed macrophages)
	serous cavities
	(pleural and peritoneal macrophages)

hydrolases (such as acid phosphatase) and cationic proteins, as well as peroxidase (called "myeloperoxidase"), and an antibacterial substance called "lysozyme"; and b) *specific* (or *secondary*) *granules*. These are smaller and less dense, and contain alkaline phosphatase, lysozyme, and lactoferrin (an antibacterial, iron-binding protein) but no lysosomal hydrolases and no peroxidase. The cytoplasm of neutrophils contains large amounts of glycogen: remember that glycolysis is the major (90%) mechanism for energy production in these cells. This is important, because it allows the cell to function effectively in damaged tissues or exudates where the oxygen supply is often poor.

Mononuclear phagocytes arise as *promonocytes* in the bone marrow; they enter the blood as *monocytes* and eventually become *macrophages* in the tissues: for example in connective tissue (where they are commonly called "histiocytes"), liver (Kupffer cells), lung (alveolar macrophages), lymphoid tissues (free and fixed macrophages), or in serous cavities (pleural and peritoneal macrophages). The phagocytic cells of the body were grouped by Aschoff into what he termed the "*Reticulo-Endothelial System*." Today it is realized that this term is inappropriate and should be replaced by the "*Mononuclear Phagocyte System*" (Figure 45). However, old habits die hard, and it may be a long time before pathologists stop referring to the "R-E System." Macrophages characteristically contain large numbers of heterogeneous dense granules. These granules contain acid hydrolases and are probably "secondary lysosomes" resulting from the fusion of the primary lysosomes with phagocytic vacuoles. Another typical feature of macrophages is the presence of abundant small pinocytic ("drinking") vesicles. Monocytes and macrophages obtain their energy from respiration and glycolysis. Oddly enough, macrophages in different situations develop different metabolic properties; alveolar macrophages, for instance, show greater rates of oxygen consumption than do peritoneal macrophages.

Phagocytosis can be subdivided into three phases (Figures 46, 47): *attachment* of particles to the cell surface, *ingestion* of particles by the cell, and *destruction* of particles within the cell (including the killing of bacteria).

a) Attachment Phase of Phagocytosis We do not really understand how a phagocyte recognizes what it should eat. A special mystery is how it knows when to cannibalize a worn-out or damaged host cell – one of its own kind. For bacteria it is apparent that special coating or *opsonization* of the particle surface is required for attachment to the phagocyte. There are two main groups of opsonic serum factors. First, there are heat-stable IgG_1 and IgG_3 *specific antibodies* directed against surface components of the particles. Second, there are heat-labile opsonic fragments of the *third component (C3) of the serum complement system* (see p. 44). After binding of opsonin molecules to the particle surface, the particle then sticks to the phagocyte surface because the phago-

Figure 46. Four remarkable frames from a phase contrast motion picture in which a human neutrophil phagocytizes a *Bacillus megaterium*.

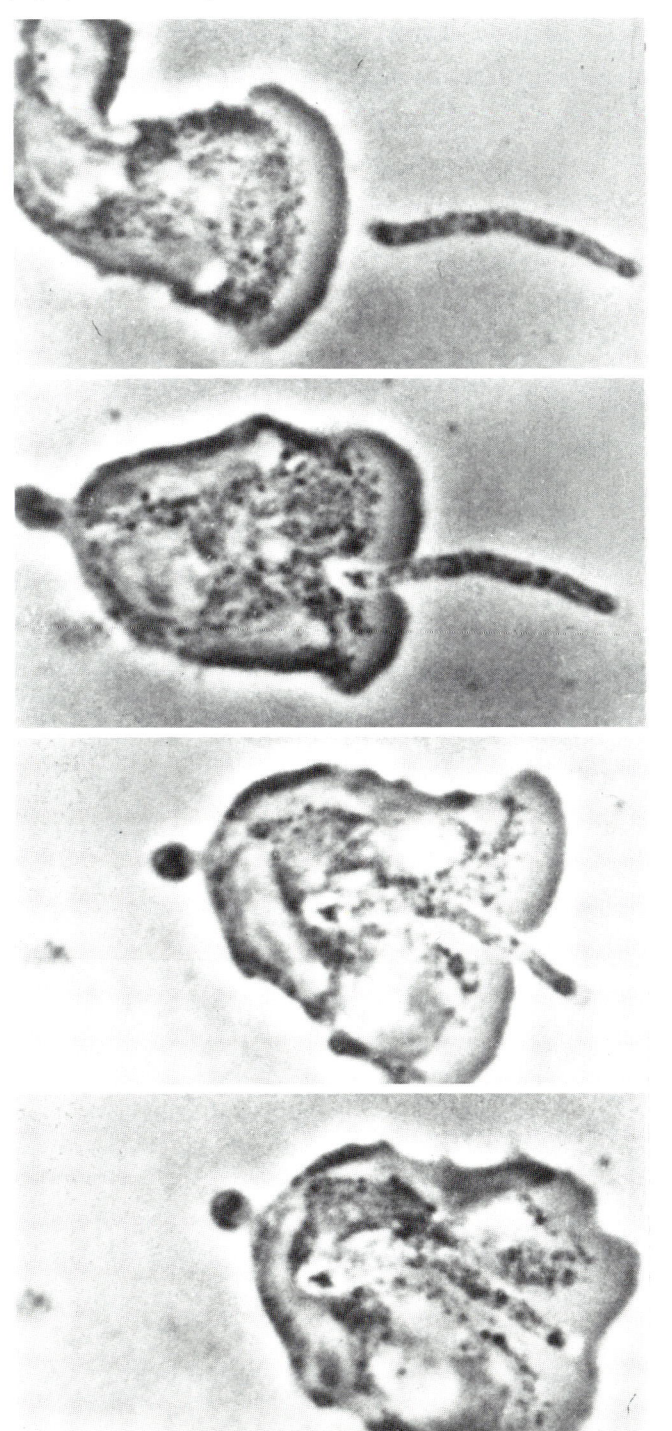

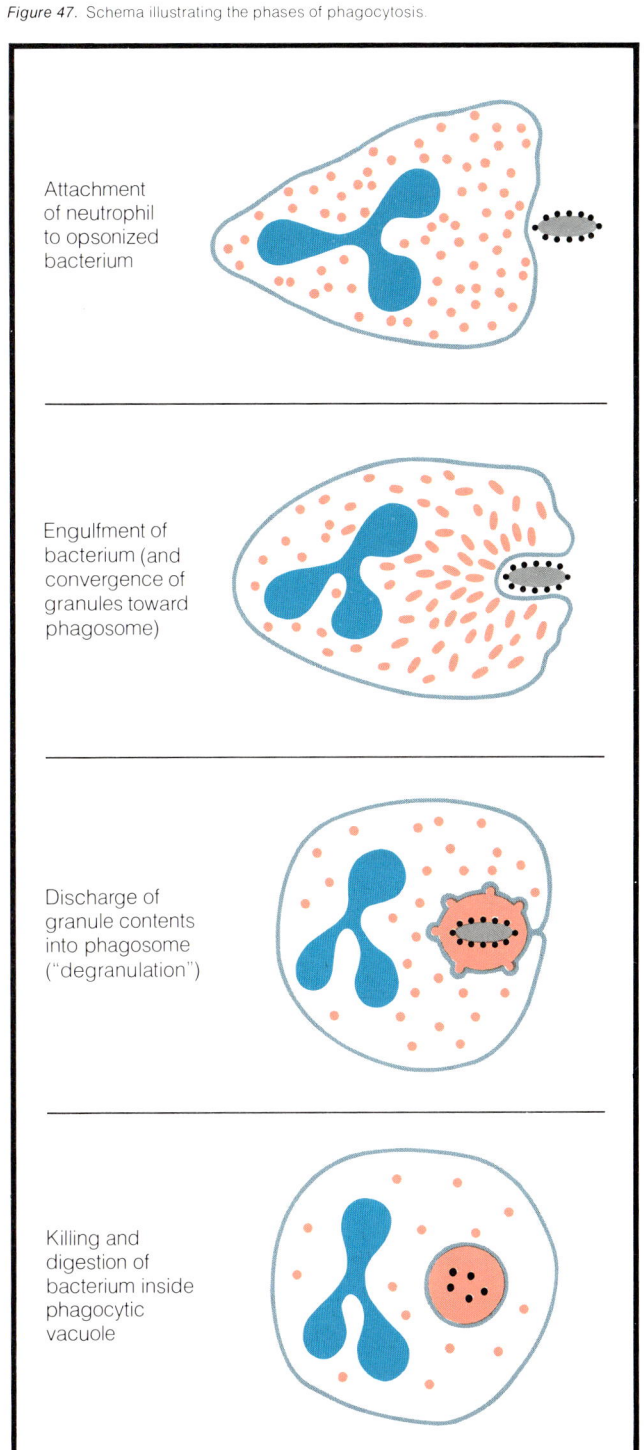

Figure 47. Schema illustrating the phases of phagocytosis.

Attachment of neutrophil to opsonized bacterium

Engulfment of bacterium (and convergence of granules toward phagosome)

Discharge of granule contents into phagosome ("degranulation")

Killing and digestion of bacterium inside phagocytic vacuole

35

Figure 48. A mononuclear phagocyte (or macrophage) which has ingested many streptococci, and (before fixation) was about to phagocytize the coccus at the lower right.

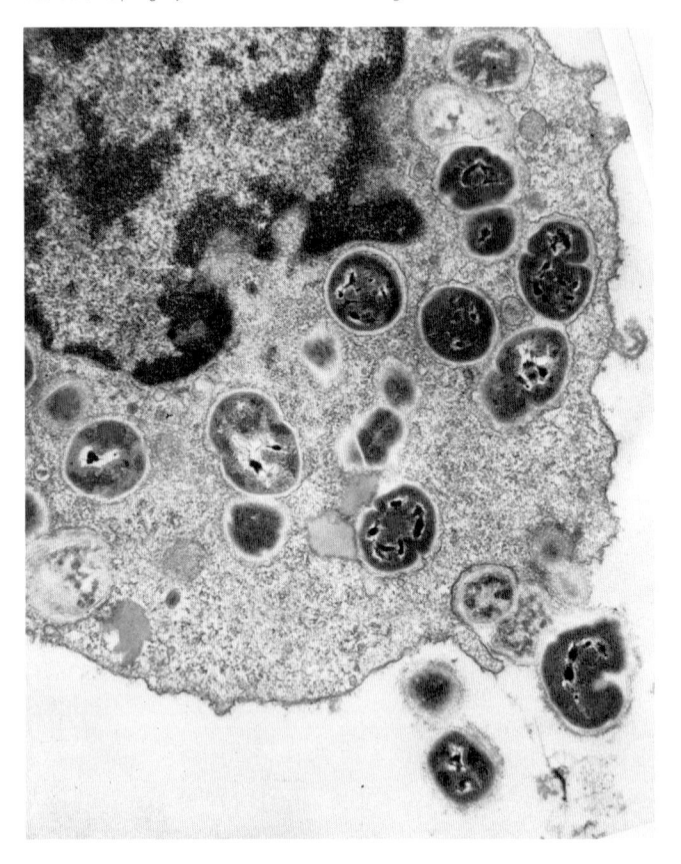

cyte has receptors for antibody molecules (attachment occurs via the Fc part of the antibody molecule) and receptors for the opsonic C3 fragments.

b) Ingestion Phase of Phagocytosis and Degranulation   After attachment occurs, the particle is internalized by the phagocyte. First, the cell extends small pseudopods (projections) which become closely applied to the surface of the particle. The pseudopods pinch together, and then fuse around the particle, thus forming a *phagosome* which is then drawn into the cell (Figure 48). As the phagosome is being formed, the cell's cytoplasmic granules converge on it, fuse with it, and discharge their contents into the space around the particle. This process is called *degranulation*. As we shall see later, granule contents are often released to the outside of the cell during phagocytosis, probably because leakage occurs from incompletely closed phagosomes.

c) Processes Leading to the Breakdown of Particles

Inside the Phagocytic Vacuole – Bacterial Killing   Phagocytosis is an energy-requiring process that is accompanied by a tremendous burst of metabolic activity in the cell. Oxygen consumption increases twofold to threefold. The amount of glucose metabolized *via* the hexose monophosphate pathway (HMP) increases to 10% from a resting level of 1%, and larger quantities of hydrogen peroxide (H_2O_2) are produced by the cell. When we consider the defects of leukocytic function, we shall see how this metabolic response is a vital element in the phagocyte's ability to destroy bacteria.

How does the metabolic burst occur? There is some dispute about this. Some investigators believe that it depends upon an NADPH oxidase which catalyzes the oxidation of NADPH, forming H_2O_2 and the $NADP^+$ that is required for operation of the HMP. However, the best evidence seems to favor the view that the key enzyme involved is *NADH oxidase* (Figure 49). This catalyzes the oxidation of NADH, forming H_2O_2 and NAD^+. The HMP is then stimulated by one or more of three possible pathways (Figure 49). First, there may be transhydrogenation [$NAD^+ + NADPH \rightleftharpoons NADH + NADP^+$] to produce the $NADP^+$ needed for the HMP. This is probably important in human neutrophils. Second, a slight excess of pyruvate could (in association with NADPH-linked lactate dehydrogenase) oxidize NADPH to $NADP^+$ at low pH, and third, some of the H_2O_2 generated by the NADH oxidase may oxidize reduced glutathione (GSH) to yield oxidized glutathione (GSSG) which in turn oxidizes NADPH to $NADP^+$.

How are bacteria killed inside the phagocytic vacuole?

Although lysosomal hydrolytic enzymes (discharged into the phagocytic vacuole from azurophil granules) can degrade digestible material, including dead bacteria, they are unlikely to be a major cause of microbial death. Instead, antimicrobial activity is due to an array of other factors (Figure 50). These include: a) the *acid pH* inside the vacuole; b) *cationic proteins* (such as *phagocytin*) from azurophil granules; c) *lysozyme* (a lytic enzyme found in the azurophil and specific granules); d) *lactoferrin* (from specific granules); e) *superoxide anion*, a highly reactive radical derived from the one electron reduction of oxygen inside the cell; and f) *hydrogen peroxide* (particularly in association with myeloperoxidase and halide ions).

Figure 49. Metabolic changes in a neutrophil during phagocytosis.

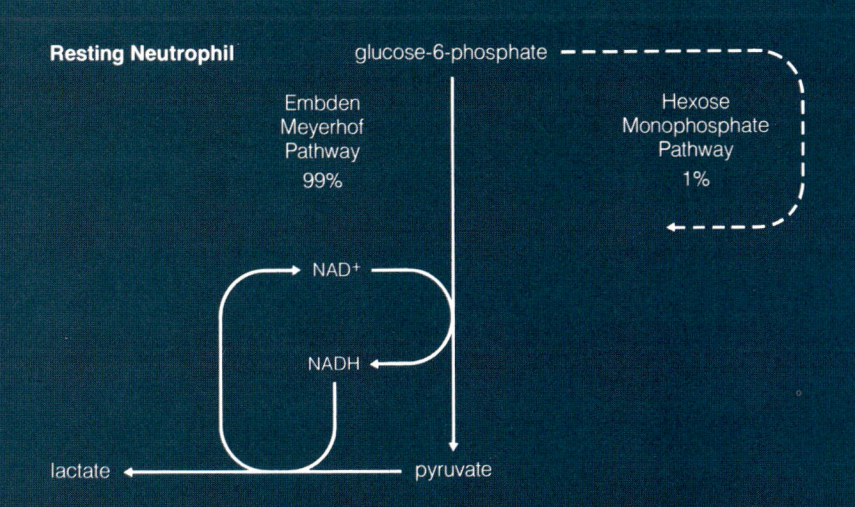

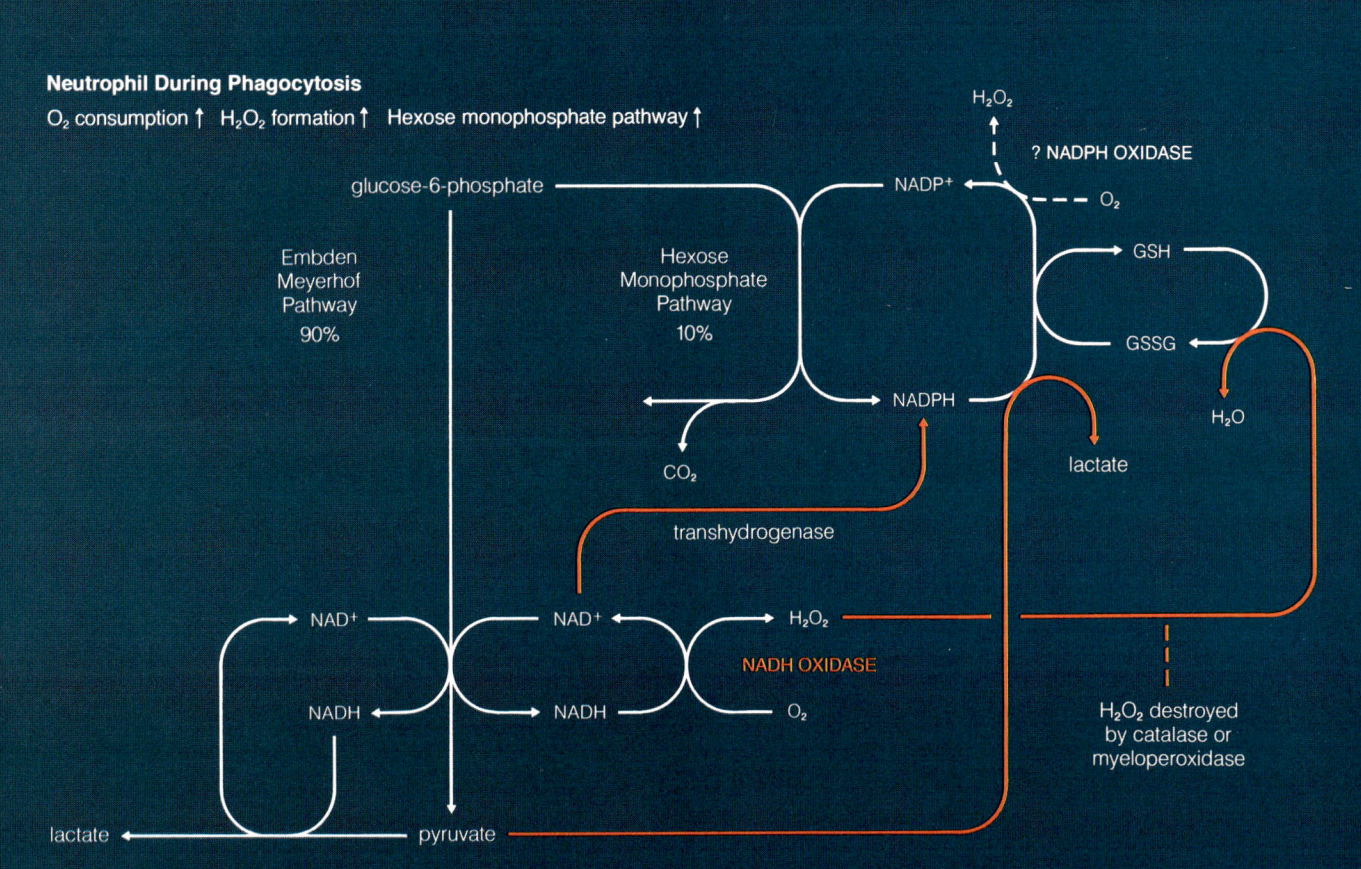

37

Defects of Leukocytic Function

Figure 50. Microbicidal agents inside phagocytic vacuole.

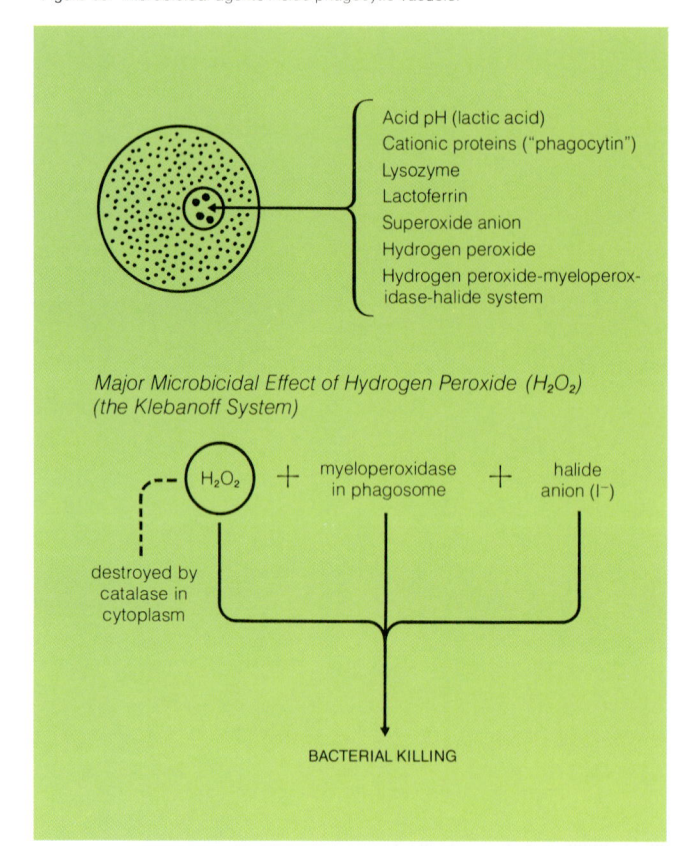

- Acid pH (lactic acid)
- Cationic proteins ("phagocytin")
- Lysozyme
- Lactoferrin
- Superoxide anion
- Hydrogen peroxide
- Hydrogen peroxide-myeloperoxidase-halide system

Major Microbicidal Effect of Hydrogen Peroxide (H_2O_2) (the Klebanoff System)

H_2O_2 + myeloperoxidase in phagosome + halide anion (I^-) → BACTERIAL KILLING

destroyed by catalase in cytoplasm

H_2O_2 is the dominant component in the neutrophil's microbicidal armamentarium. In 1967, Seymour Klebanoff clearly showed that the effectiveness of H_2O_2 (against bacteria, fungi, and viruses) is greatly enhanced by myeloperoxidase (from azurophil granules) and halide ions (I^-, Cl^-, or Br^-) (Figure 50). How this H_2O_2-myeloperoxidase-halide system actually works is not certain. The microbes may be damaged by iodination (if I^- is used), or chloramines or toxic aldehydes may be formed. Whatever mechanisms are involved, there is no doubt about the importance of the system (discussed in the section on *chronic granulomatous disease* p. 60).

Incidentally, the cell is faced with an interesting technical problem during phagocytosis: how to protect itself from the effects of excessive free H_2O_2. It apparently does this in two ways: a small amount may be used up in the oxidation of reduced glutathione (see Figure 49), but most is broken down in the cytoplasm by catalase.

For many years, physicians have wondered why certain individuals suffer repeated infections. Recently, it has been realized that many of these patients have either too few or functionally abnormal leukocytes. For instance, neutrophils may show abnormal locomotion; they may show defective phagocytosis; there may be impaired intracellular killing of microbes; and so on. Figure 51 sets out the major defects and matches them with particular clinical syndromes.

Neutropenia

This is a shortage of neutrophils in the blood. Usually it occurs in patients with diseases affecting the bone marrow: a) *Leukemias* – malignant cells crowd out the normal hemopoietic tissue. b) *Drug-induced agranulocytosis* – a low neutrophil count occurs as an abnormal reaction to certain drugs (such as chloramphenicol). c) *Cyclic neutropenia* – a rare and obscure condition in which very low blood neutrophil counts occur at regular intervals (the lowest counts being recorded every 21 days). The disorder is associated with recurrent infections, especially in the skin and middle ear.

Neutropenia may also be found in patients with severe defects of leukocytic locomotion (for example in the "lazy leukocyte syndrome"), and is perhaps due to an inability of the leukocytes to leave the bone marrow.

Disorders of Migration and Chemotaxis

Leukocytes from these patients do not crawl properly – not surprisingly, therefore, inflamed sites show only sparse leukocytic infiltration. Such disorders can be classified into three groups: a) defects in the cells themselves (the intrinsic cellular dysfunctions); b) defects due to the presence of inhibitors of locomotion; and c) defects resulting from a lack of chemotactic factors.

a) Intrinsic Cellular Dysfunctions   In this group, the cells have an underlying abnormality that somehow results in impaired locomotion. It has been claimed that in many such patients there is an inability to respond to a chemotactic gradient, but the evidence for this is rather weak – chemotaxis was tested using the Boyden system without rigorously excluding a consideration of diminished ability of the cells to crawl randomly.

Chediak-Higashi syndrome – an autosomal recessive disease in which the leukocytes contain gigantic azuro-

Figure 51.

Defects of Leukocytic Function

Defect	Major Clinical Syndromes
Neutropenia (too few neutrophils)	• Leukemias • Drug-induced agranulocytosis • Cyclic neutropenia
Disorders of migration and chemotaxis	• Intrinsic cellular dysfunctions (something wrong with the cells) *Chediak-Higashi syndrome* *Lazy leukocyte syndrome* *Job's syndrome* *Diabetes mellitus* • Inhibitors of locomotion *Inhibitors in serum* *Drugs (eg, corticosteroids)* • Deficiencies of chemotactic factors *Complement deficiencies* *Chemotactic factor inactivators in serum*
Disorders of phagocytosis	• Opsonin deficiencies *Hypogammaglobulinemia* *Complement deficiencies (C3)* *Sickle cell disease* • Impaired engulfment *Drugs (eg, morphine analogs)* • Impaired degranulation (impaired discharge of granule contents into phagosome) *Chediak-Higashi syndrome* *Drugs (eg, colchicine, corticosteroids, antimalarials)*
Disorders of microbicidal (killing) mechanisms	• Impaired H_2O_2 production *Chronic granulomatous disease* *Glucose-6-phosphate dehydrogenase deficiency* *Drugs (eg, hydrocortisone, sulfonamides)* • Myeloperoxidase deficiency

phil granules. Such cells show impaired locomotion and poor degranulation. Patients with this disorder have an increased susceptibility to infections.

"Lazy leukocyte syndrome" – apparently due to a primary defect in leukocyte locomotion. It is associated with neutropenia and recurrent infections.

"Job's syndrome" – typically affects fair-skinned, red-haired girls. It is characterized by recurrent "cold" staphylococcal abscesses, hence the name: "So went Satan forth from the presence of the Lord, and smote Job with sore boils from the sole of his foot unto his crown" (Job 2:7).

Diabetes mellitus – leukocytes from diabetic patients show impaired locomotion. This impairment is apparently correctable by incubating the cells in a medium containing insulin and glucose.

b) Inhibitors of Leukocytic Locomotion Extrinsic factors may inhibit leukocytic locomotion.

Inhibitors in serum – when tested *in vitro*, serum from certain patients inhibits locomotion of leukocytes from normal individuals. Some of these patients show no other distinguishing feature (apart from recurrent infections) but others have been found to have rheumatoid arthritis (inhibition may be due to the effects of rheumatoid factor complexes in serum), or raised serum IgE levels.

Drugs – certain drugs (corticosteroids, quinoline derivatives, phenylbutazone, etc.) have been reported to impair leukocytic movement.

c) Deficiencies of Chemotactic Factors These may be due to deficiencies of chemotactic factor precursors or to inactivation of factors after they are formed.

Complement deficiencies – genetic deficiencies or abnormalities may affect C3 or C5, the complement components that generate chemotactic fragments (see section on Mediators). Patients with these deficiencies may show an increased susceptibility to infection, but this is probably due mainly to deficient opsonizing capacity of the serum rather than to a lack of chemotactic agents. In fact, in sites of infection, complement-derived chemotactic fragments are probably not essential for leukocytic infiltration, because bacteria themselves release strong chemotactic factors.

Chemotactic factor inactivators (CFI) – these are found in small amounts in normal human serum; they apparently inactivate chemotactic fragments of C3 and C5 as well as bacterial chemotactic factors. Strikingly high levels of CFI have been reported in patients with Hodgkin's disease. In contrast, abnormally low levels have been found in patients with pulmonary emphysema combined with α_1-antitrypsin deficiency. This finding may be relevant to the pathogenesis of emphysema.

Disorders of Phagocytosis

These can be subdivided into three groups: a) defective attachment due to inadequate opsonization of the microbe; b) impaired engulfment; and c) defective discharge of granule contents into the phagosome (impaired degranulation).

a) Opsonin deficiencies

These constitute a clinically important group of diverse diseases:

Hypogammaglobulinemia – a lack of specific antibodies.

Complement deficiencies – especially prevalent in certain patients with a lack of C3. (Note: newborn infants, especially if premature, tend to be susceptible to infection. This may be due to temporarily low complement levels.)

Sickle cell disease – such patients may show an increased susceptibility to pneumococcal septicemia (bacteria in the blood) and pneumococcal meningitis, due to a specific lack of opsonin for pneumococci.

b) Impaired engulfment

Drugs – morphine analogs can cause impaired ingestion by phagocytes.

c) Impaired degranulation

Chediak-Higashi syndrome – the giant cytoplasmic granules fail to fuse normally with phagosomes, resulting in defective degranulation and decreased discharge of granule contents into the phagocytic vacuole.

Drugs – colchicine, corticosteroids, and antimalarial drugs have been reported to impair degranulation.

A particularly intriguing failure of granule-phagosome fusion occurs when normal macrophages phagocytize viable *Mycobacterium tuberculosis* or *Toxoplasma gondii* organisms. It is not clear why this occurs but it obviously favors long-term survival of the organisms in normal hosts and may be a significant factor in the pathogenesis of tuberculosis.

Disorders of Microbicidal Mechanisms

The importance of Klebanoff's H_2O_2-myeloperoxidase-halide system (Figure 50) in microbial killing is emphasized when we examine the causes of defective microbicidal function. There are two main possibilities: a) impaired H_2O_2 production, and b) myeloperoxidase deficiency.

a) Impaired H_2O_2 Production This occurs in the following conditions:

Chronic granulomatous disease (CGD) – this is the most dramatic example of impaired H_2O_2 production. It was first recognized as a distinct clinical entity in 1957. In 1966, it was realized that CGD was due to a leukocytic microbicidal defect.

CGD is an inherited disease usually affecting males. Children with this condition suffer multiple recurrent granulomatous infections of the skin, lymph nodes, lung (pneumonia), bones (osteomyelitis), etc. They often die before they reach seven years of age.

The major defect in CGD patients is that their leukocytes fail to show the burst of metabolic activity that usually accompanies phagocytosis. This failure is probably due to a lack of NADH oxidase in the cells (Figure 49). The cells, therefore, do not make H_2O_2, and this leads to a failure of the H_2O_2-myeloperoxidase-halide microbicidal system.

Certain bacteria normally produce catalase (which destroys H_2O_2), whereas other bacteria do not. Interestingly, CGD patients develop serious infections with catalase-producing bacteria (such as *Staphylococcus aureus*), but not with catalase-negative bacteria (such as pneumococci). This occurs because the catalase-negative bacteria commit suicide: they produce enough free H_2O_2 (from their own metabolic machinery) for the H_2O_2-myeloperoxidase-halide system to work inside the phagocytic vacuole (Figure 52). On the other hand, the catalase manufactured by catalase-positive bacteria destroys the small amounts of H_2O_2 that the bacteria produce, and thereby saves their lives (Figure 52). In a fascinating experiment, Johnston and Baehner showed that *Staphylococcus aureus* (catalase-positive) organisms were killed inside CGD leukocytes if the cells were also allowed to ingest latex spherules coated with glucose oxidase (which acts as a potent H_2O_2 generator inside the cell).

Figure 52. Chronic granulomatous disease (CGD).
Schema illustrating how the H_2O_2-myeloperoxidase-halide system of
a normal neutrophil kills a bacterium (left); how a CGD neutrophil
(no H_2O_2) is incapable of killing a catalase-producing bacterium (middle);
how a CGD neutrophil kills a catalase-negative bacterium (right).

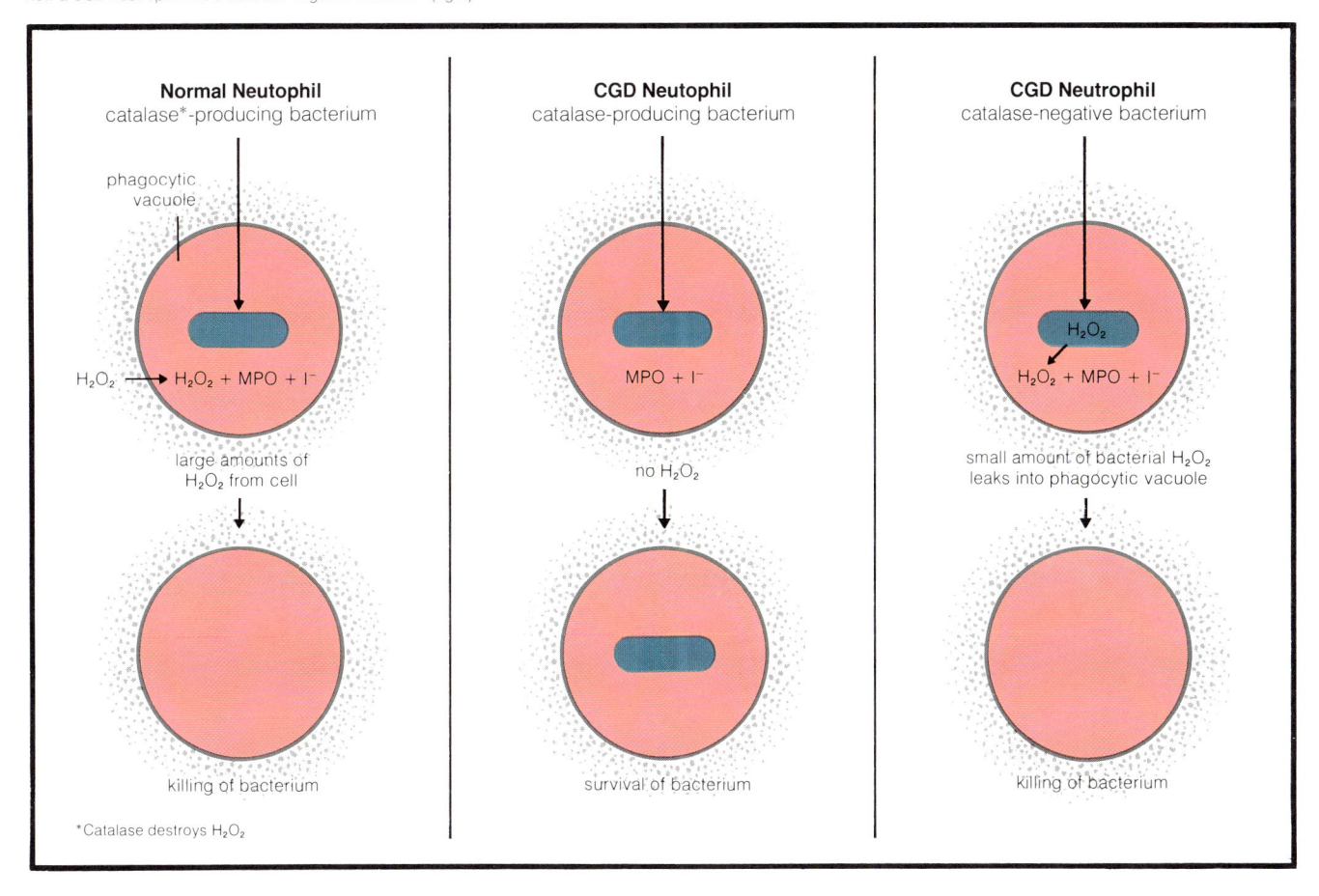

Normal Neutophil
catalase*-producing bacterium

phagocytic vacuole

$H_2O_2 \rightarrow H_2O_2 + MPO + I^-$

large amounts of H_2O_2 from cell

killing of bacterium

*Catalase destroys H_2O_2

CGD Neutophil
catalase-producing bacterium

$MPO + I^-$

no H_2O_2

survival of bacterium

CGD Neutrophil
catalase-negative bacterium

H_2O_2
$H_2O_2 + MPO + I^-$

small amount of bacterial H_2O_2 leaks into phagocytic vacuole

killing of bacterium

The NBT Test is a useful diagnostic test for CGD. Oxidized nitroblue tetrazolium (NBT), a yellow compound, is added to phagocytizing neutrophils. The dye enters the phagocytic vacuoles, and in normal cells is reduced to a dark blue formazan that can be seen under a microscope. The mechanism involved has not been established. CGD neutrophils show defective reduction of NBT during phagocytosis.

Glucose-6-phosphate dehydrogenase (G6PD) deficiency – this condition is another possible cause of defective H_2O_2 production in cells. However, such patients only have significant problems with infections if the G6PD level is near zero.

Drugs – hydrocortisone and certain sulfonamides can interfere with H_2O_2 production in leukocytes. Such a mechanism (along with impaired locomotion and degranulation) may be responsible for the predisposition to infection found in patients on prolonged corticosteroid therapy.

b) Myeloperoxidase (MPO) Deficiency Although sometimes associated with recurrent infections, such a defect does not usually lead to any ill effects. Myeloperoxidase cooperates with H_2O_2 in microbicidal function but it also breaks down H_2O_2. Therefore, a lack of MPO may lead to the intracellular accumulation of increased H_2O_2 that can act directly as a microbicidal agent.

The study of defective leukocytic function is a field of extraordinary interest. One can safely predict a great expansion in the number and kinds of defects that will be reported over the next few years. Hopefully, one may also gain further insights into the mechanisms involved and possibly some clues as to corrective therapy.

Mediators of Inflammation

Now that we have described the main events of acute inflammation, how are they caused?

The inflammatory reaction is a response, and the two main responding agents are blood vessels and cells. So the key question can now be phrased as follows: how do the vessels and the cells – in and around the injured area – receive the order to respond?

There can be only two kinds of messages, as far as we know: through nerves and by means of chemical agents. Both are involved, but the chemical pathway is by far the most important. The chemical messengers are generally known under the name of *mediators* of the inflammatory response. We can subdivide these into *exogenous* mediators (coming from outside the body) and *endogenous* mediators (coming from inside the body). Foremost among the exogenous mediators are bacterial products, which can be directly responsible for vascular leakage or attraction of leukocytes, and which certainly play a role in the response to bacterial infection. The endogenous mediators, however, are of more general interest and importance; we shall deal with them in some detail.

The story of the endogenous mediators begins in the 1920s with the classical and very simple experiments of Sir Thomas Lewis in London. When the skin was "firmly stroked with a bluntly pointed instrument," three things happened: 1) A *red reaction* appeared within seconds along the line of pressure. Lewis attributed this reaction to a local dilatation of the small blood vessels of the area. 2) A bright red *flare* developed 15 to 30 seconds later and spread several centimeters from the initial line of pressure (Figure 53). This apparently resulted from widespread arteriolar dilatation. 3) A local edema popularly termed a *wheal* was seen within 1 to 3 minutes (Figure 53). This was due to increased vascular permeability.

Lewis called this sequence *The Triple Response*. He postulated that a diffusible mediator, either histamine or an "H-substance" (for "histamine-like substance") was liberated in the tissues along the line of injury. This mediator acted directly on local blood vessels to produce the red reaction and then the wheal. Lewis thought that it might also cause the flare by means of an *axon reflex*: stimulation of nerve endings in the skin causes impulses to travel up sensory nerves and then loop back (through "arteriolar collateral" branches) to induce arteriolar dilatation (Figure 54). Evidence favoring this axon

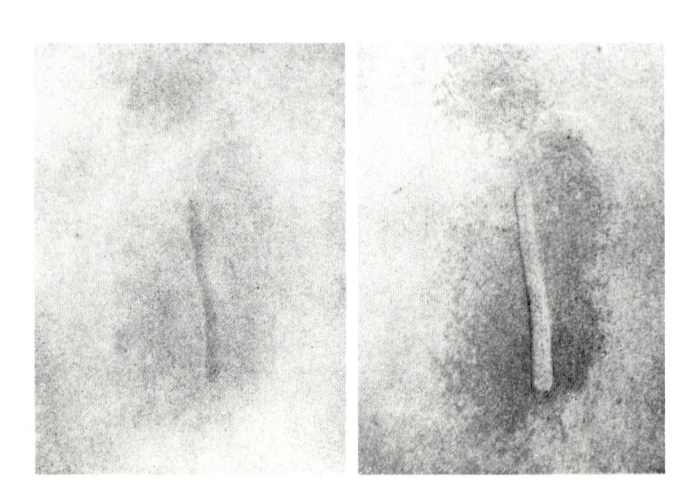

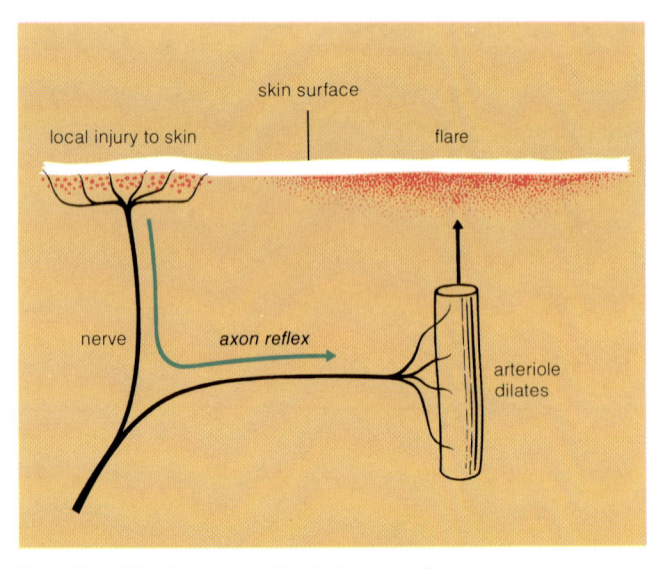

Figure 53. (top) The development of the "triple response," as photographed for Sir Thomas Lewis' book *The Blood Vessels of the Human Skin and Their Responses* (1927). *Left:* The skin has been firmly stroked and, at the same time, a single intradermal injection of histamine has been administered (left): "The photograph, taken 1½ minutes after stimulation, shows the dark red line of the stroke and a diffuse surrounding flare; the needle prick is likewise surrounded by a flare. No wheals have appeared as yet." *Right:* "The same skin at the end of 3½ minutes. The flares surrounding the two stimuli are now brighter and more sharply defined and whealing has nearly reached its full height."

Figure 54. (bottom) Schema of the axon reflex.

reflex idea included Lewis' demonstration that the flare occurred if the sensory nerve trunks were recently cut but not if the nerves were allowed time to degenerate. However, even today we are not sure whether this mechanism is valid or not. As to the identity of Lewis' "H-substance," it is unlikely to be histamine alone because antihistaminic drugs do not abolish the triple response. However, such objections are trivial. The important thing is that Lewis' work conferred scientific credibility upon the concept of mediators and, as such, it is a landmark in the field of inflammation.

Endogenous mediators can be classified into two major groups (Figure 55): those from plasma and those from tissues.

Factors Released from Plasma

Plasma contains three interconnected mediator-producing systems (Figure 55): a) the kinin system, b) the complement system, and c) the clotting system.

a) Kinin System   In 1955, Sir Ashley Miles and Don Wilhelm discovered that a permeability-inducing factor was produced when serum was diluted. They called this factor "PF/dil." However, it was soon realized that the key step in the development of this factor was not the dilution (which simply diluted an inhibitor of the PF) but was the contact of the serum with the glass tubes in which the dilution was performed. Margolis then showed that glass triggered the Hageman factor (factor XII of the clotting system). It is now known that the activation of factor XII leads to the formation of kinins.

What are the steps in kinin production? – A schema of the kinin system is shown in Figure 56. It is useful to remember that the kinin sequence (like the cascade of reactions that occurs in clotting) and in complement activation consists of a series of enzymatic steps in which there is progressive amplification in the numbers of molecules involved. It starts in a small way but finishes by producing large numbers of end-product molecules – in this case, kinins. It begins when the Hageman factor is activated by contact with any of a host of substances, including glass, kaolin, collagen, basement membrane, cartilage, sodium urate crystals, trypsin, kallikrein (a later component of the kinin system), plasmin (the enzyme that dissolves fibrin), clotting factor XI, and bacterial lipopolysaccharides (endotoxins). Once it is acti-

Figure 55.

Classification of Endogenous Mediators of Inflammation

Origin	Major Groups	Major Mediators
Plasma	Kinin system	bradykinin
	Complement system	C3 fragments
		C5 fragments
		C$\overline{567}$ complex
	Clotting system	fibrinopeptides
		fibrin degradation products
Tissues	Vasoactive amines	histamine
		5-hydroxytryptamine (5-HT)
	Acidic lipids	slow-reacting substance of anaphylaxis (SRS-A)
		prostaglandins
	Lysosomal components	cationic proteins
		acid proteases
		neutral proteases
	Lymphocyte products	migration inhibitory factor (MIF)
		chemotactic factors
		lymphotoxin
		skin reactive factors
		mitogenic factor
		lymph node permeability factor
	Others	eg, endogenous pyrogens leukocytosis factors

vated, the Hageman factor has three very important effects. First, it triggers the clotting cascade (by activating factor XI). Second, it triggers the fibrinolytic system (by activating plasminogen proactivator to give plasminogen activator, which converts plasminogen to plasmin). Third, it has "prekallikrein activator" (PKA) activity. PKA (probably a fragment of the Hageman factor) activates prekallikrein to form kallikrein. Kallikrein then cleaves kininogen to produce a kinin called "bradykinin." Bradykinin is a peptide consisting of 9 amino acids. It tends to be rapidly broken down by kininases, which are peptidases present in plasma and tissues.

Figure 56.

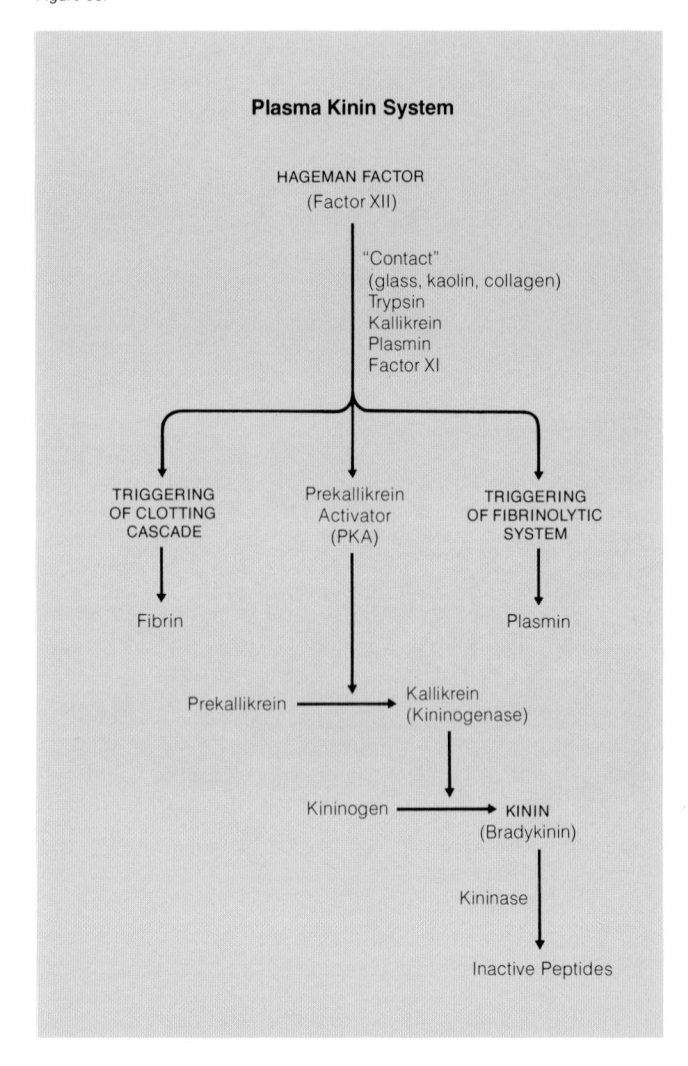

Plasma Kinin System

HAGEMAN FACTOR
(Factor XII)

"Contact"
(glass, kaolin, collagen)
Trypsin
Kallikrein
Plasmin
Factor XI

TRIGGERING OF CLOTTING CASCADE → Fibrin

Prekallikrein Activator (PKA)

TRIGGERING OF FIBRINOLYTIC SYSTEM → Plasmin

Prekallikrein → Kallikrein (Kininogenase)

Kininogen → KININ (Bradykinin)

Kininase ↓ Inactive Peptides

What are the effects of bradykinin? In very low doses, it causes 1) slow (hence the name: *bradykinin*) contraction of certain kinds of smooth muscle *in vitro*; 2) dilatation of blood vessels *in vivo* (thus inducing a fall in systemic blood pressure if injected intravenously); 3) pain when applied to the base of a blister or when injected into the skin; 4) increased vascular permeability at sites of injection.

Bradykinin does not attract leukocytes when tested in the Boyden chemotaxis system. In contrast, it has been claimed that kallikrein and plasminogen activator are chemotactic for neutrophils and mononuclear phagocytes.

b) Complement System In 1910, Friedberger incubated fresh serum with antigen-antibody precipitates and then injected the serum into the circulation of an animal. The animal quickly developed a severe reaction that resembled systemic anaphylaxis. Such serum obviously contained a toxin – Friedberger called it "anaphylatoxin." We now know that this toxin provokes an anaphylactic reaction because it causes an explosive release of histamine and other mediators from mast cells and basophils. Such serum has been shown to induce 1) contraction of smooth muscle *in vitro*; 2) local vascular leakage if injected into the skin; 3) attraction of leukocytes (in the Boyden system).

All of these properties are due to by-products generated by the interaction of antigen-antibody complexes with the serum complement system.

What is the complement system? The serum complement system consists of nine major components. The steps involved in the activation of these components are shown in Figure 57 which illustrates the so-called classical complement sequence (delineated from studies of lysis of sheep erythrocytes exposed to rabbit antibodies). Here again (as in the clotting and kinin systems), there is a beautiful, progressive amplification in the number of molecules involved in the various steps. The first component, C1 (consisting of three subunits: C1q, C1r and C1s), is activated by the immune complex to form C1 esterase which, in turn, acts upon C4 and then C2. This produces $C\overline{42}$ enzyme (also called C3 convertase), which cleaves C3 into C3a fragments (released into the medium) and C3b fragments. The C3b fragments bind to the surface of the cell, forming $C\overline{423}$ enzyme. This interacts with C5 (cleaving off C5a fragments, followed by C6 and C7 (producing a complex of $C\overline{567}$).

Finally, there is binding of C8 and C9, and this leads to membrane damage and lysis of the cell. This classical pathway, involving C1, C4 and C2, with the production of C3 convertase, is activated by most antigen-antibody complexes and by certain nonimmunologic agents such as plasmin and trypsin.

The alternate pathway of complement activation – In certain circumstances C3 can be activated without involving C1, C4 and C2. This occurs when there is triggering of the serum "properdin system" (originally described by Pillemer and his associates in 1954 and recently "redis-

Figure 57.

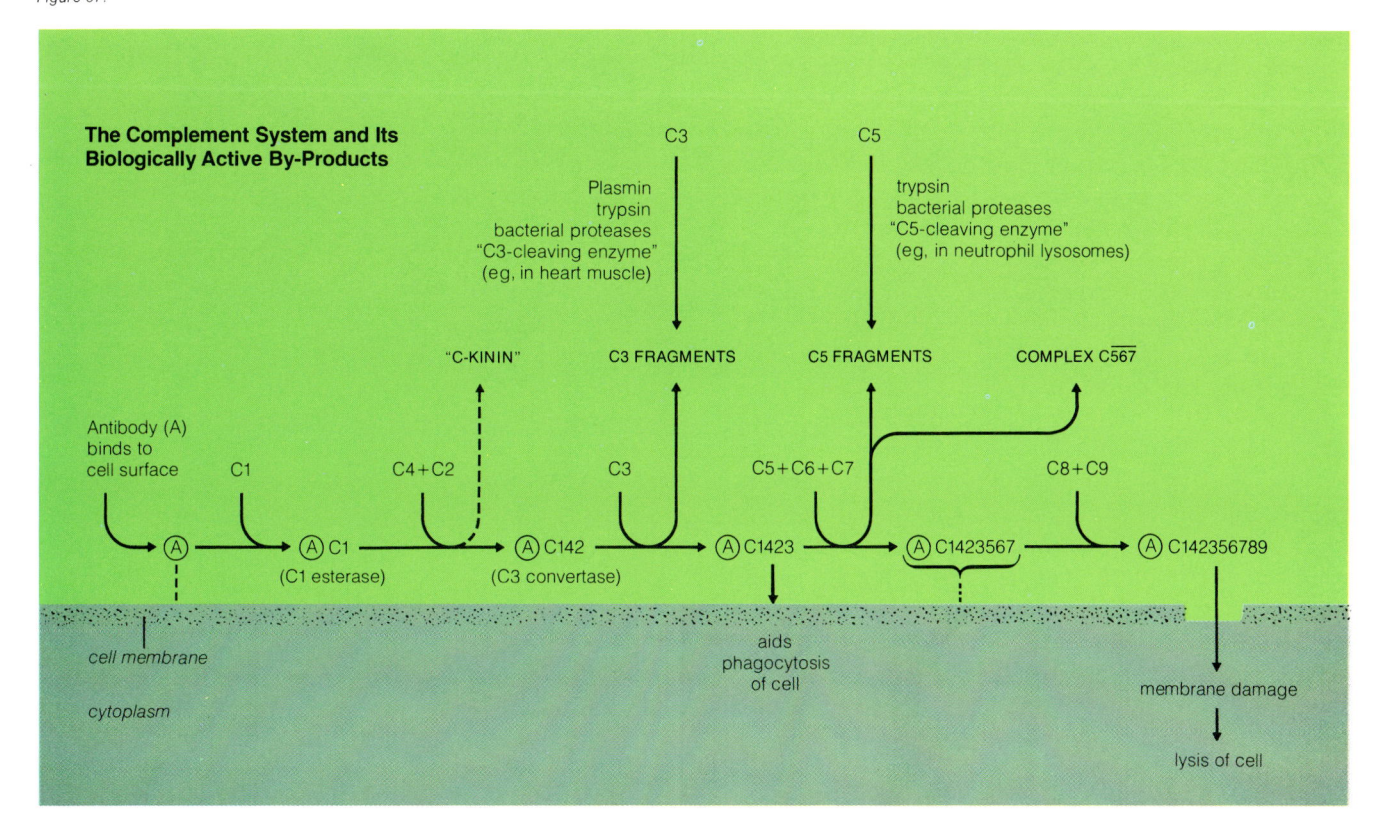

The Complement System and Its Biologically Active By-Products

covered" as the "C3-activator system" – Figure 58), for instance, when there is interaction of serum with certain kinds of antigen-antibody complexes, various polysaccharides, bacterial lipopolysaccharides (endotoxins), and cobra venom. In this "alternate pathway," various serum components (such as properdin, factor A, factor B, etc.) have been identified, but the activation steps are not yet clearly defined.

Control mechanisms – The complement cascade is held under control in two ways: 1) some of its component enzymes are unstable; and 2) serum contains various inhibitors or inactivators, eg, C1 esterase inhibitor (which is absent in patients with hereditary angioneurotic edema) and C3 inactivator (which acts to control both the classical and alternate pathways).

What does complement have to do with inflammation? It is very likely that the serum complement system plays an important role in the inflammatory response, particularly (but certainly not exclusively) in immunologically mediated reactions involving antigen-antibody complexes. The reason for this is that biologically active by-products are liberated from complement components after activation of the sequence (by either the classical or alternate pathways) (Figure 59). Such by-products can be produced also by the direct action of various "extra-complementary" enzymes on either C3 or C5 (Figure 57). These by-products are as follows: 1) *C3 fragments* – these are low molecular weight factors released during complement activation or from cleavage of C3 by plasmin, trypsin, bacterial proteases, or "C3-cleaving enzymes" found in various tissues. 2) *C5 fragments* – these are low molecular weight factors released during complement activation or from cleavage of C5 by trypsin, bacterial proteases, or "C5-cleaving enzymes" found in lysosomes of neutrophils, platelets, and perhaps other types of cells. 3) *Complex C$\overline{567}$* – this is a high molecular weight complex of C5, C6 and C7, produced only during the sequential activation of the complement system. 4) *"C-kinin"* –

this is a kinin-like peptide (possibly derived from cleavage of C2) that has been isolated from the plasma of patients with hereditary angioneurotic edema.

The inflammatory effects of the complement system by-products – As shown in Figure 59, these are:

1) *Increased vascular permeability* – This has been attributed to the formation of "anaphylatoxins" in the serum – anaphylatoxin activity has been found in C3a fragments and C5a fragments. They act mainly as histamine-releasing agents. If injected into human skin, they induce local reddening and vascular leakage. In such studies C5a is 1000 times more active than C3a.

2) *Chemotactic attraction of leukocytes* – This is probably the most important effect of the complement by-products. Hurley and Spector provided the first real indication that chemotactic factors could be derived from serum components. In 1961 these workers observed a rapid, massive infiltration of neutrophils into the skin of rats injected with serum that previously had been incubated with minced tissues. They proposed that a tissue factor acted upon a serum substrate to produce a product that caused leukocytic emigration. In 1962, Boyden published his filter membrane method for assessing the chemotactic activity of substances in solution and showed that a chemotactic factor was produced by the interaction of antigen-antibody complexes with serum. Then, as discussed earlier, Hurley used the Boyden system to demonstrate the chemotactic activity of serum that had been activated by minced tissues. It was subsequently confirmed (by direct observation of cellular locomotion in slide-coverslip preparations) that neutrophils were attracted towards fragments of tissue that had been incubated with fresh serum.

It is now clear that the chemotactic activity found in these early experiments was due to complement system by-products. At one stage, there was some conflict in the literature over which of the by-products were of most importance in chemotaxis. At first, Peter Ward and his colleagues proposed that $\overline{C567}$ was the chemotactic agent produced when antigen-antibody complexes interacted with serum. However, later work by Sorkin's group and Snyderman's group suggested that C5 fragments were more important in such circumstances. This view, favoring C5 fragments as the major complement-derived chemotactic factors, has since become widely accepted,

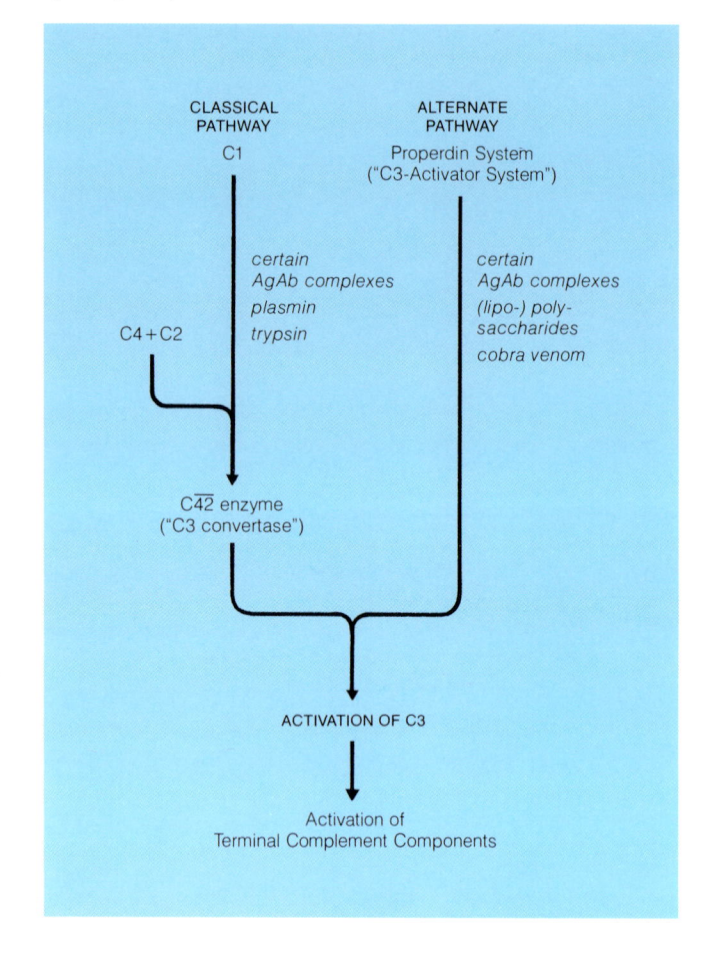

Figure 58. (top) Schema illustrating complement activation: the *classical* pathway and the *alternate* pathway.
Figure 59. (bottom)

Major Inflammatory Effects of Complement System By-Products

Complement By-Products	Vascular Leakage	Chemotaxis of Neutrophils	Others
C3 fragments	+	+	leukocytosis
C5 fragments	+	+	neutrophil lysosomal enzyme release
$\overline{C567}$ complex	−	+	−

although it is also likely that both C$\overline{567}$ and C3 fragments may be chemotactic agents in certain situations. (Incidentally, it is not known for certain whether the chemotactic fragments of C3 and C5 are the same as the anaphylatoxins C3a and C5a.)

When damaged tissue interacts with serum, the chemotactic factors that form may be derived from both C3 and C5, because C3- and C5-cleaving enzymes are present in various cell types. In some very interesting and clinically relevant studies, Ward and his co-workers have found chemotactic C3 fragments in recent myocardial infarcts and in synovial fluids of patients with inflammatory nonrheumatoid joint disease. Chemotactic C5 fragments (and C$\overline{567}$) were also found in synovial fluids of patients with rheumatoid arthritis and in immunologically damaged blood vessels.

We have been discussing chemotaxis of neutrophils. What about other kinds of leukocytes? Experiments using the Boyden system indicate that serum incubated with antigen-antibody complexes is also chemotactic for mononuclear phagocytes and for eosinophils. Interestingly, treatment of fresh serum with heat-killed *Mycobacterium tuberculosis* organisms leads to the formation of chemotactic activity for mononuclear phagocytes. This could help to explain the persistent infiltration of macrophages in tuberculous lesions.

3) *Other "inflammation-related" effects of complement by-products* — Complement by-products may have other effects. For example, C3 fragments can induce *leukocytosis* (by provoking "neutrophil release" from the bone marrow reserve); C5 fragments may induce the release of lysosomal enzymes from neutrophils.

c) Clotting System There are two potential inflammatory mediators derived from the clotting system: 1) Fibrinopeptides (released from fibrinogen molecules by the action of thrombin during clotting). These may induce vascular leakage and be chemotactic for neutrophils. 2) Fibrin degradation products (released during the proteolysis of fibrin by plasmin) may well be chemotactic for neutrophils.

Such mediators could contribute to the inflammatory response in certain diseases that are inhibited by treatment with anticoagulant drugs. These diseases include certain kinds of glomerular injury and delayed hypersensitivity reactions.

Interconnections Between the Kinin System, the Complement System and the Clotting System There are interactions among all of these systems, forming what Oscar Ratnoff has appropriately called a "tangled web." The schema illustrating these links (Figure 60) looks awesomely complex. However, it becomes simpler to understand if one looks primarily at the effects of PLASMIN (an enzyme generated from plasminogen, either after activation of Hageman factor, or by an interaction with other agents such as bacterial factors, a urine factor, or cellular factors, eg, from neutrophils or certain endothelial cells). Indeed most of the interconnections of the web occur through plasmin, as follows (Figure 61): 1) It digests fibrinogen and fibrin (fibrinolysis). 2) It "feeds back" to activate the Hageman factor (particularly triggering kinin production). 3) It activates C1 to form C1 esterase (in the classical pathway of the complement sequence). 4) It cleaves C3 to give anaphylatoxic and chemotactic C3 fragments.

Other links in the web: kallikrein and clotting factor XI activate Hageman factor. In addition, activation of the kinin system produces a so-called Kf fragment that apparently helps C1 esterase to produce C3 convertase. Conversely, it seems that activation of the complement system can affect the Hageman factor empire: more specifically, it triggers clotting, a reaction that may explain why certain immunologically induced renal diseases are associated with striking intravascular clotting and fibrin deposition in glomeruli.

It is worth noting that most of the information about these pathways and effects has been obtained from *in vitro* studies. It may not be valid to expect them to work this way *in vivo*. The best illustration of this is Hageman factor deficiency. The plasma from such patients clots poorly in glass tubes but the patients themselves usually have no particular bleeding tendency. In fact, the original Mr. Hageman died with thrombotic embolism in the lungs! It is also interesting that such patients show normal inflammatory responses. This indicates either that bradykinin is an insignificant inflammatory mediator in humans, or that kinin activation (like clotting) can occur *in vivo* without Hageman factor, or that other mediators can take over the role of bradykinin whenever necessary.

Hereditary Angioneurotic Edema This is an inherited disorder characterized by recurrent bouts of ede-

Figure 60. Schema of the interrelationships between the kinin, clotting, fibrinolytic, and complement systems.

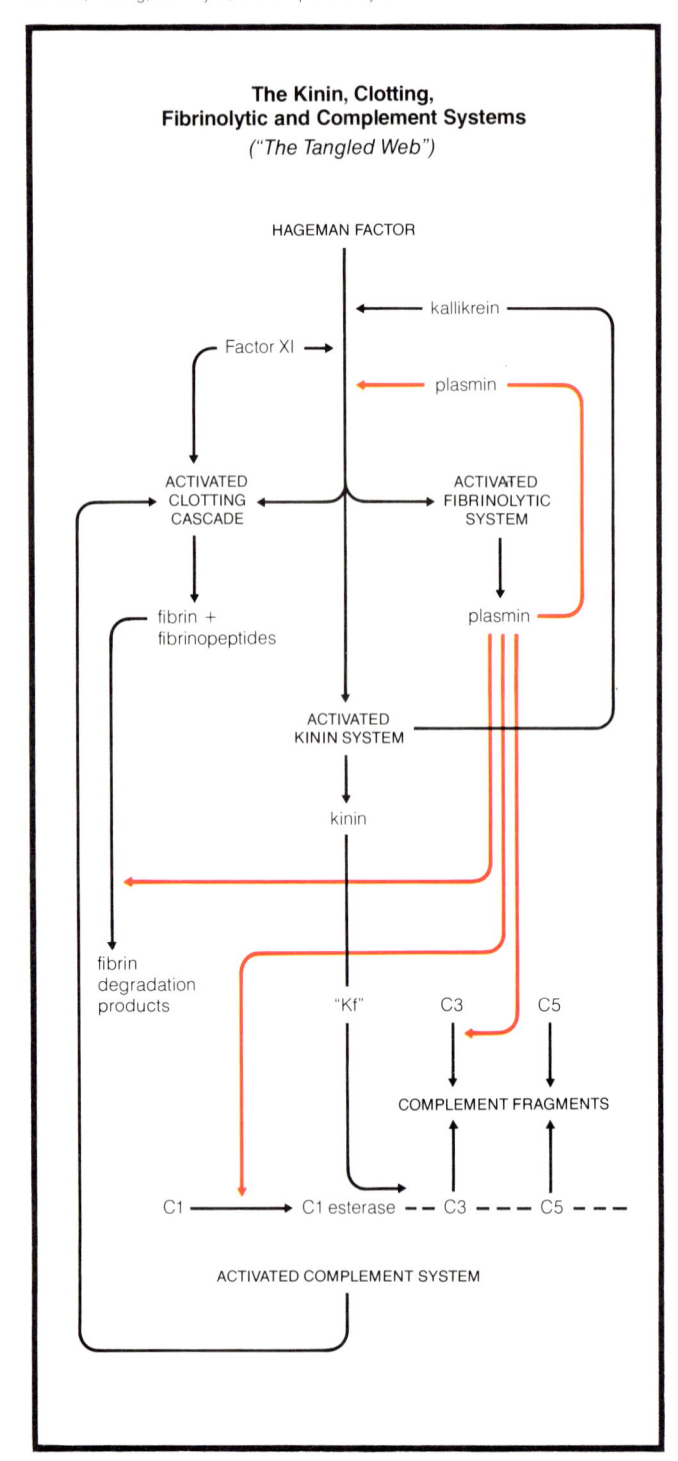

ma, often provoked by emotional stress. The edema can occur in the skin, the gastrointestinal tract (producing pain), and/or in the larynx (sometimes choking the patient). The disease is due primarily to a lack of C1 esterase inhibitor in the serum. How does this cause edema? In addition to its effect on C1 esterase, the inhibitor is also known to normally inhibit the formation and activity of kallikrein and plasmin. The most popular concept is that the edematous attacks are due to an episodic activation of plasmin which, in the absence of the inhibitor, induces the following: 1) Activation of Hageman factor, leading to unrestricted formation of bradykinin. 2) Activation of C1, leading to unrestricted complement activation (aided by "Kf"), with the production of "C-kinin" (with bradykinin-like activity) and perhaps the anaphylatoxins C3a and C5a (although histamine release due to the anaphylatoxins is unlikely to be significant because antihistamine drugs do not affect the attacks). We are therefore dealing with an inflammatory form of edema.

This idea of the central role of plasmin in the pathophysiology of hereditary angioneurotic edema is strongly supported by the observation that attacks are prevented by treatment with ε-amino caproic acid, which inhibits the conversion of plasminogen to plasmin.

Factors Released from Tissues

We can classify the tissue-derived inflammatory mediators into the following groups (Figure 55): a) vasoactive amines, b) acidic lipids, c) lysosomal components, d) lymphocyte products, and e) others.

a) Vasoactive Amines (Histamine, 5-Hydroxytryptamine) Histamine is present in the granules of mast cells, basophils, and platelets; it is also found in the parietal region of the stomach. 5-hydroxytryptamine (5-HT, or serotonin) is present in mast cells (of rats and mice) and platelets as well as in the mucosa of the gut and in the brain.

Mast cells (in German, *mästen* means "to stuff" or "to fatten") are found mainly in loose connective tissues. They were discovered in 1877 by Paul Ehrlich when he noticed that certain cells stained metachromatically *(red)* with a blue-violet dye. This metachromatic reaction is due to the presence of sulfated mucopolysaccharides in the abundant cytoplasmic granules of these cells. Such granules appear dense or dark in electron micrographs

Figure 61. (top) Schema illustrating the effects of plasmin.
Figure 62. (bottom left) A human mast cell. Note the dense granules.
Figure 63. (bottom right) Mast cells: some normal, some degranulating (in center of picture) in a rat mesentery stained with toluidine blue.

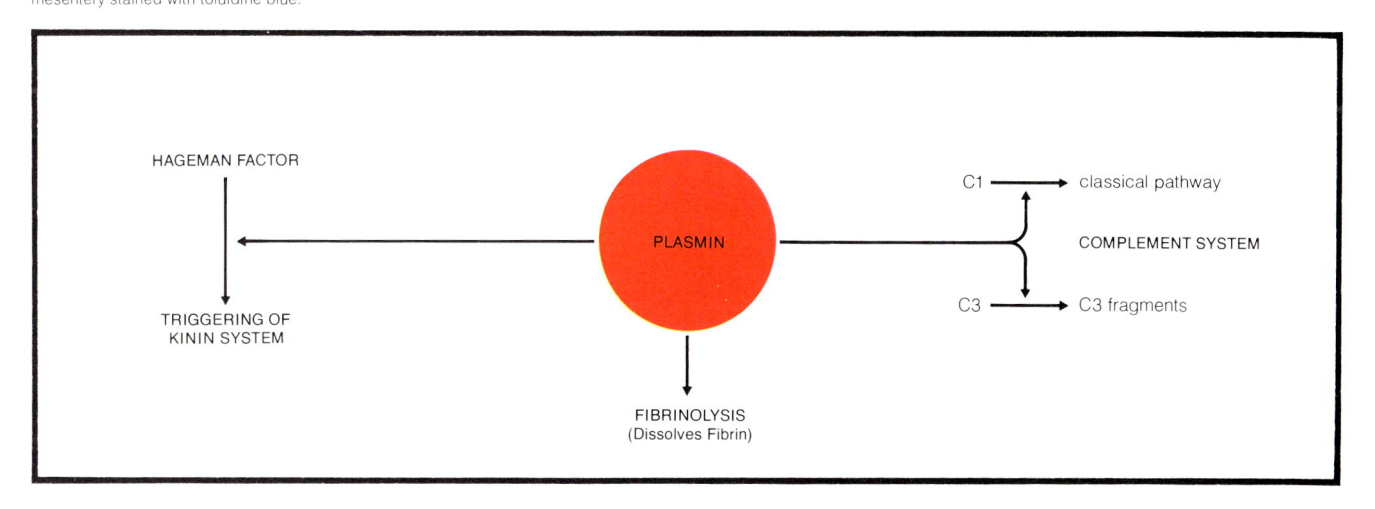

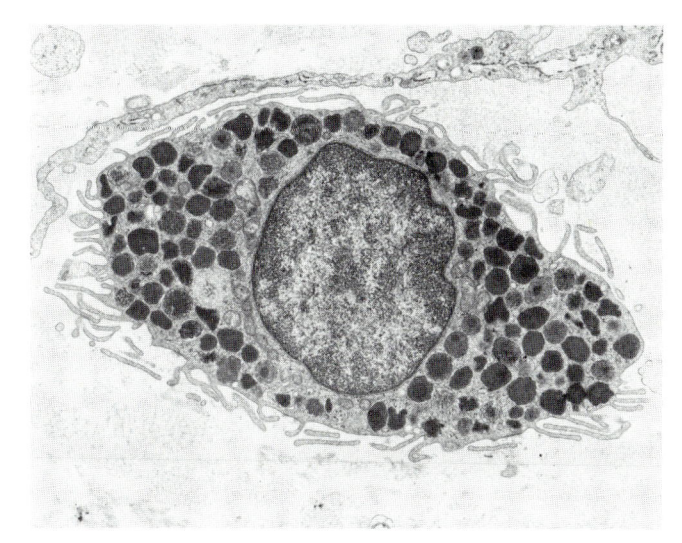

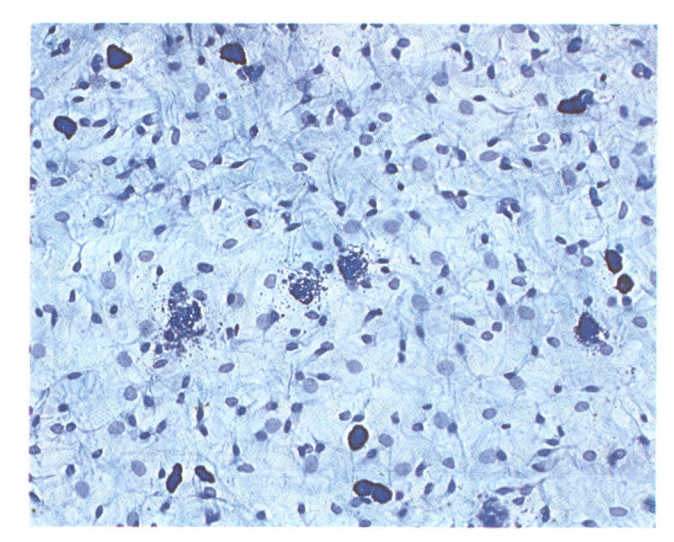

(Figure 62). They contain heparin (an acid mucopolysaccharide with striking anticoagulant properties), histamine, 5-hydroxytryptamine (in rodents) and a variety of proteins and enzymes. When mast cells are injured or appropriately triggered, degranulation occurs, either by extrusion of granules or by discharge of granule contents into the surrounding environment (Figure 63). One may now ask, "What is the physiological function of mast cells?" The answer is not known, although a host of theories have been proposed, ranging from secretion (releasing heparin into the blood) to endocytosis (the uptake and detoxification of histamine). There is little doubt, however, that mast cell products are involved in inflammation and anaphylactic reactions. An interesting clinical entity in which mast cells play a key role is *urticaria pigmentosa*. Patients with this condition have large numbers of mast cells in their skin (along with some pigmentation), and rapidly develop wheals (urticaria, or "hives") because mild mechanical irritation of the skin is sufficient to cause mast cell degranulation.

Amines (and other products) are released from mast cells in response to the following: 1) Physical injury — mechanical trauma, heat, irradiation; 2) Certain chemical agents — "histamine-liberators" (such as 48/80), toxins, snake venoms, bee venom, trypsin, surfactants, dextran, polyvinylpyrrolidone (PVP), and perhaps more relevant to inflammatory responses, a neutrophil lysosomal cationic protein. 3) Immunological processes – antigenic challenge of homocytotropic antibody (IgE)-sensitized cells, or exposure to anaphylatoxins (C3a and C5a).

Release from platelets (the "platelet release reaction") occurs in response to a variety of stimuli: thrombin, collagen, antigen-antibody complexes, gamma globulin-coated surfaces, snake venom, epinephrine, and ADP. In addition, amines can be released from platelets by a process called "leukocyte-dependent histamine release." The antigen reacts with IgE on the surface of circulating basophils which release (along with amines) a "platelet activating factor" (PAF) that, in turn, induces amine release from platelets. It has been proposed that this leukocyte-dependent histamine release from platelets aids the deposition of circulating antigen-antibody complexes in arteries (causing arteritis) or in the glomerulus (producing a type of glomerulonephritis).

The mechanisms involved in these release reactions are interesting. Of particular importance and clinical relevance is the release that occurs in *systemic anaphylaxis*, with the rapid onset of potentially lethal bronchospasm, laryngeal edema and/or shock. This can occur when someone who is sensitive to antigen, such as penicillin, is inadvertently exposed to that antigen. In such cases, homocytotropic antibody (IgE in humans) becomes bound to the surface of mast cells (and basophils). Then, if these cells are exposed to the offending antigen, the antigen molecules form bridges between adjacent IgE molecules. This leads to a series of intracellular biochemical events that result in the secretion of mediators. The major mediators released in this reaction can be subdivided into two groups (Figure 64): 1) Preformed mediators (already present in the mast cell granules before stimulation and released within seconds), which include histamine and an "eosinophil chemotactic factor of anaphylaxis," ECF-A (an acidic peptide, with a molecular weight of approximately 500, that attracts eosinophils when tested in the Boyden system). 2) Newly synthesized mediators (not detected before stimulation, but rapidly synthesized, and then released a few minutes after antigenic challenge); these include "slow reacting substance of anaphylaxis" (SRS-A) and "platelet activating factor" (PAF).

Figure 64. Major mediators released from IgE-sensitized human mast cells when exposed to specific antigen.
Figure 65. (bottom)

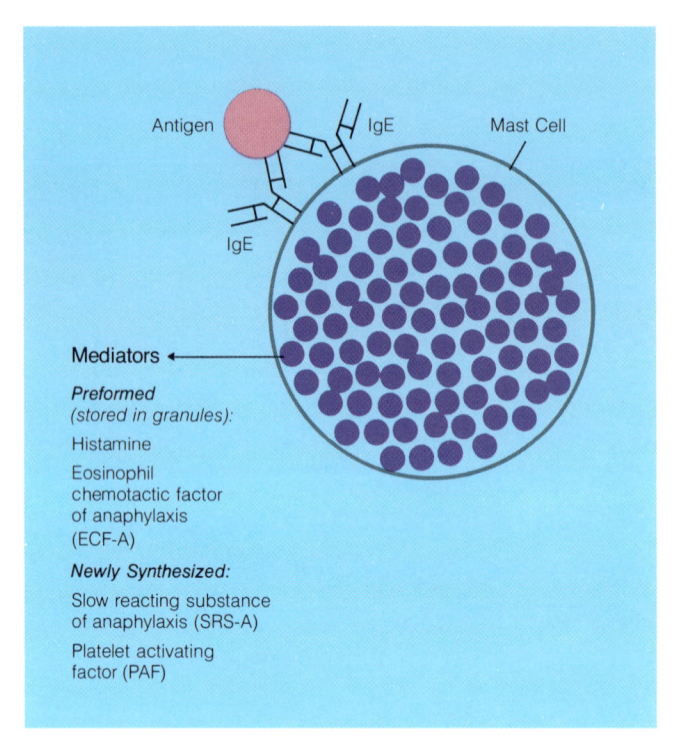

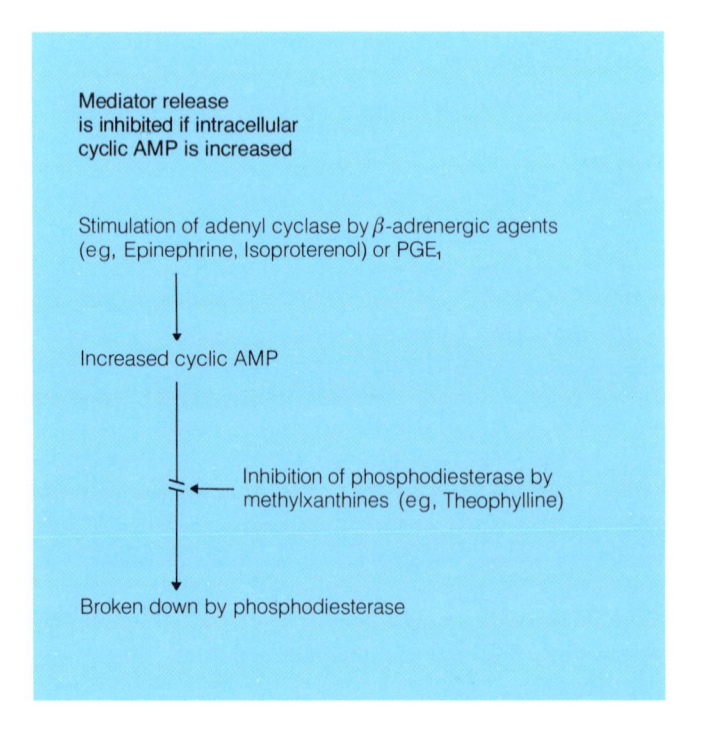

In addition, it is likely that prostaglandins are also released in such reactions.

Release of certain of these mediators (such as SRS-A) can be inhibited if intracellular levels of cyclic AMP are increased by treatment with β-adrenergic agents (epinephrine, isoproterenol), methylxanthines (theophylline) and certain prostaglandins (PGE$_1$) (Figure 65). This probably explains why epinephrine, isoproterenol, theophylline, and similar drugs are useful clinically in treatment of immediate hypersensitivity reactions.

What are the inflammatory effects of the vasoactive amines? Both histamine and 5-HT produce contraction of smooth muscle and also increase vascular permeability. However, neither has any chemotactic effect on leukocytes in the Boyden system.

b) *Acidic Lipids (SRS-A and Prostaglandins)* This group includes:

Slow reacting substance of anaphylaxis (SRS-A) – In 1938, Feldberg and Kellaway found that during perfusion of guinea pig or cat lungs, treatment with cobra venom led to the appearance of what they called "slow reacting substance" (SRS) in the effluent. This SRS was characterized by its peculiar ability to produce a slow and prolonged contraction of smooth muscle preparations, in contrast with the more rapid and transient effects of histamine. Kellaway and Trethewie then discovered a pharmacologically similar substance in the effluent of immunologically sensitized guinea pig lungs treated with specific antigen *in vitro*. Brocklehurst coined the term "slow reacting substance of anaphylaxis" (SRS-A) to distinguish it from SRSs produced by nonimmunologic mechanisms. (*Note*: it is possible that such nonimmunologic SRSs are, in fact, prostaglandins.)

SRS-A is an acidic, sulfur-containing lipid. Its molecular weight is approximately 400. As mentioned, it is released from appropriately sensitized cells that have been challenged with antigen. The most significant studies in this field have been those of Frank Austen's group in Boston on the effects of antigenic challenge on human lung fragments passively sensitized *in vitro* with IgE. Incidentally, such release of SRS-A is accompanied by liberation of other mediators (Figure 64): histamine, eosinophil chemotactic factor of anaphylaxis (ECF-A), platelet activating factor (PAF), and prostaglandins.

In anaphylaxis, the most important effect of SRS-A is

Figure 66. The structure of prostaglandin E$_1$.

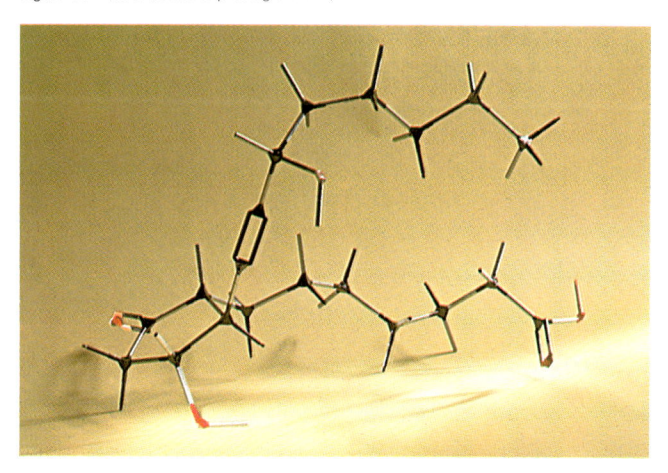

probably the contraction of bronchiolar smooth muscle, thus causing narrowing and obstruction of the airways. SRS-A may also potentiate the effects of histamine in causing either laryngeal edema or bronchiolar contraction; it can induce vascular leakage, but it has no chemotactic activity for leukocytes.

Histologic examination of the tissues of patients with allergic reactions reveals the presence of large numbers of eosinophils. Since it appeared that neither histamine nor SRS-A was chemotactic for eosinophils, a search was made for the responsible mediator. This led to the discovery of eosinophil chemotactic factor of anaphylaxis (ECF-A). Human eosinophils (but not neutrophils) contain large amounts of aryl sulfatase, the only enzyme known to destroy SRS-A. The infiltration by eosinophils may therefore be the body's way of trying to protect itself from the deleterious effects of excessive SRS-A.

Prostaglandins (PGs) – In recent years there has been an explosion of interest in the prostaglandins. These are long chain C$_{20}$ compounds that are synthesized in cells from polyunsaturated fatty acids. They belong to various groups (E, F, A, B, etc.) on the basis of structure (Figure 66). Although they are found practically everywhere in the body, their full significance as pharmacologic agents has not yet been clearly defined.

It is likely that prostaglandins are involved, at least to some extent, in inflammatory processes. Thus, PG-like activity is found in inflammatory exudates, and PGs are released from neutrophils during phagocytosis. The following inflammation-related effects of PGs have been re-

Figure 67.

Inflammatory Effects of Neutrophil Lysosomal Products	
Products	Effects
Cationic proteins	Increased vascular permeability
	Chemotaxis of mononuclear phagocytes
	Immobilization of neutrophils
Acid proteases	Degradation of basement membranes etc. (if pH sufficiently acid)
Neutral proteases	Degradation of: collagen elastin renal basement membrane cartilage fibrin
	Generation of chemotactic fragments from C5
	Release of kinin from plasma kininogen

ported: 1) *Increased vascular permeability* – PGE_1 and PGE_2 induce vascular leakage when injected into human or rat skin (perhaps acting by inducing histamine release from mast cells). 2) *Chemotactic activity* – it has been claimed that PGE_1 attracts neutrophils in the Boyden system. 3) *Pain* – intravenous infusions of PGs can induce headache and it has been found that PGE_1 and PGE_2 cause pain if injected into human skin. In very low doses, PGs seem to sensitize the pain receptors to stimulation by touch, histamine, or bradykinin. (*Note:* Cohnheim attributed the pain of inflammation to local swelling causing pressure on nerves. This may be part of the story, but it is now obvious that endogenous mediators are also involved in triggering pain receptors.) 4) *Fever* – PGEs induce fever when injected into the third ventricle of the brain of cats, or intravenously into women (for termination of pregnancy).

Recently it has been reported that rats immunized against prostaglandins develop less edema in certain inflammatory reactions.

A particularly exciting and significant contribution to the field of endogenous mediators was the discovery by John Vane of London in 1971 that aspirin and aspirin-like drugs (indomethacin, phenylbutazone) inhibit the biosynthesis of prostaglandins. More recently, it has been found that corticosteroids inhibit the release of prostaglandins from cells but do not inhibit synthesis. These various drugs have been used for many years as anti-inflammatory, analgesic (pain-relieving), and antipyretic (anti-fever) agents. It is comforting to find plausible reasons for their effectiveness. Such discoveries also emphasize the potential importance of the PGs as natural mediators of inflammation-related events.

Another important role for PGs may be the inhibition of certain inflammatory processes. For example, PGE_1 is known to cause the accumulation of cyclic AMP inside cells by activating adenyl cyclase (the enzyme that converts ATP to cyclic AMP) (Figure 65). This accumulation of cyclic AMP could lead to inhibition of leukocytic locomotion, inhibition of phagocytic activity, inhibition of SRS-A release from mast cells in immediate hypersensitivity reactions, and inhibition of lysosomal enzyme release from neutrophils during phagocytosis. Some asthmatic patients develop fatal obstruction to their upper and lower airways when they are given aspirin or aspirin-like drugs. This may occur because the drugs cause inhibition of prostaglandin synthesis leading to decreased intracellular cyclic AMP levels, thus allowing enhanced release of SRS-A from sensitized cells.

c) Lysosomal Components In inflamed areas, a host of potentially important mediators are probably spilled out of lysosomes (from neutrophils, but also from other cells, including platelets). These include the following (Figure 67):

1) *Cationic proteins* – Some of these can induce increased vascular permeability (acting either directly or through histamine release from mast cells), chemotactic attraction of mononuclear phagocytes (when tested in the Boyden system), and immobilization of neutrophils (and eosinophils, but apparently not monocytes).

2) *Acid proteases* – It has been shown that acid proteases from neutrophil lysosomes can degrade basement membranes at acid pH *in vitro*. In inflamed areas *in vivo*, the pH tends to fall because of lactic acid production by neutrophils. However, the optimal pH for activity of the

Figure 68. Arthus reaction in skin of a guinea pig (the scale is in millimeters).

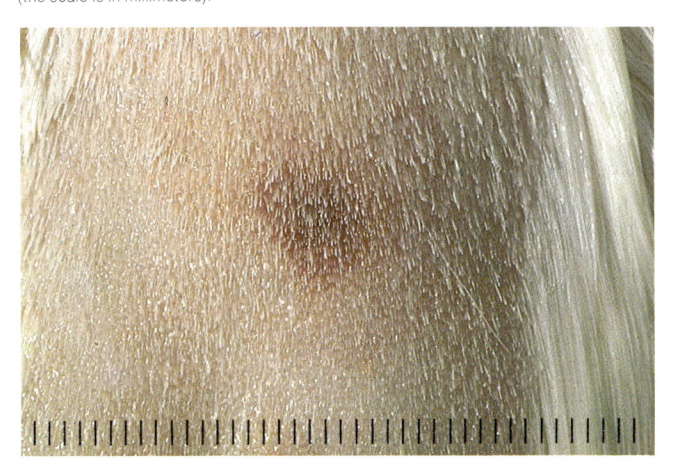

neutrophil acid proteases is around 3.0; it is unlikely that the extracellular pH falls as low as this *in vivo.* Janoff has proposed that such enzymes exert their main effect inside the neutrophil's phagocytic vacuole, and that the neutrophil proteases are responsible for extracellular damage in inflammation.

3) *Neutral proteases*—These are probably of great importance in causing tissue breakdown in a whole variety of disease processes, ranging from simple abscesses to more complicated conditions such as those involving the formation and deposition of antigen-antibody complexes in tissues (in the walls of blood vessels and in the kidneys), various forms of arthritis, and perhaps pulmonary emphysema. Here we encounter the paradox that the inflammatory response can sometimes cause more trouble than seems worthwhile; neutrophils pour into the inflamed area where they release enzymes which damage tissue elements (collagen, elastin, renal basement membrane, cartilage, fibrin). This process helps to perpetuate the inflammatory process. It is not clear why this occurs in certain circumstances but not in others. It may be related to the nature of the injured tissue (and its susceptibility to damage by neutrophil enzymes), and/or to the nature of the original inflammatory stimulus that somehow causes too many neutrophils to enter the lesion over a prolonged period of time.

It is also possible that appropriate control mechanisms are not present in patients with such diseases. For example, patients with pulmonary emphysema (a disease in which there is progressive loss of alveolar walls in the lung) commonly have a genetically determined *deficiency of α_1-antitrypsin,* a potent inhibitor of neutral protease activity. This α_1-antitrypsin is normally present in human serum, and it is logical to assume that it plays a role in limiting the unfortunate extracellular effects of the neutrophil enzymes. It has been proposed that recurrent, relatively minor lung infections in such patients can lead to unusually extensive tissue damage because of the uncontrolled effects of these neutral proteases (from neutrophils, and probably from alveolar macrophages). Not all individuals who are deficient in α_1-antitrypsin necessarily develop emphysema, but this may be explained by the recent observation that unusually low neutrophil neutral protease levels are found in certain people. An additional factor may be that emphysematous patients with α_1-antitrypsin deficiency have also been found to have a deficiency of a "chemotactic factor inactivator" in their serum. This deficiency could contribute to damage, because of the persistence of supernormal amounts of chemotactic factors leading to an inordinate delivery of neutrophils (and their enzymes) into the inflamed tissues.

Apart from causing tissue damage, neutrophil neutral proteases have been reported to generate chemotactic fragments from C5 (the fifth component of serum complement) and to produce release of kinin-like substances from a plasma kininogen. Incidentally, damaged or phagocytizing neutrophils release serum-independent factors that attract other neutrophils. These factors are presumably of lysosomal origin but as yet they have not been characterized.

The inflammatory effect of excessive numbers of infiltrating neutrophils is nicely demonstrated by the *Arthus reaction.* An antigen is injected into the skin of an animal that has high levels of precipitating antibody against the antigen. A striking inflammatory response with reddening and swelling develops within a couple of hours and reaches a peak a few hours later (Figure 68). The sequence of events is probably as follows: the injected antigen precipitates with antibody molecules in small blood vessels of the area. These complexes bind complement, and complement by-products are soon generated, causing histamine release and an intense infiltration of neutrophils. The neutrophils either die or ingest the complexes and perhaps other material, leading

Figure 69. Gout and silicosis: two examples of cytotoxic release of lysosomal components due to "internal perforation" of phagocytic vacuoles (the "suicide bag" concept).

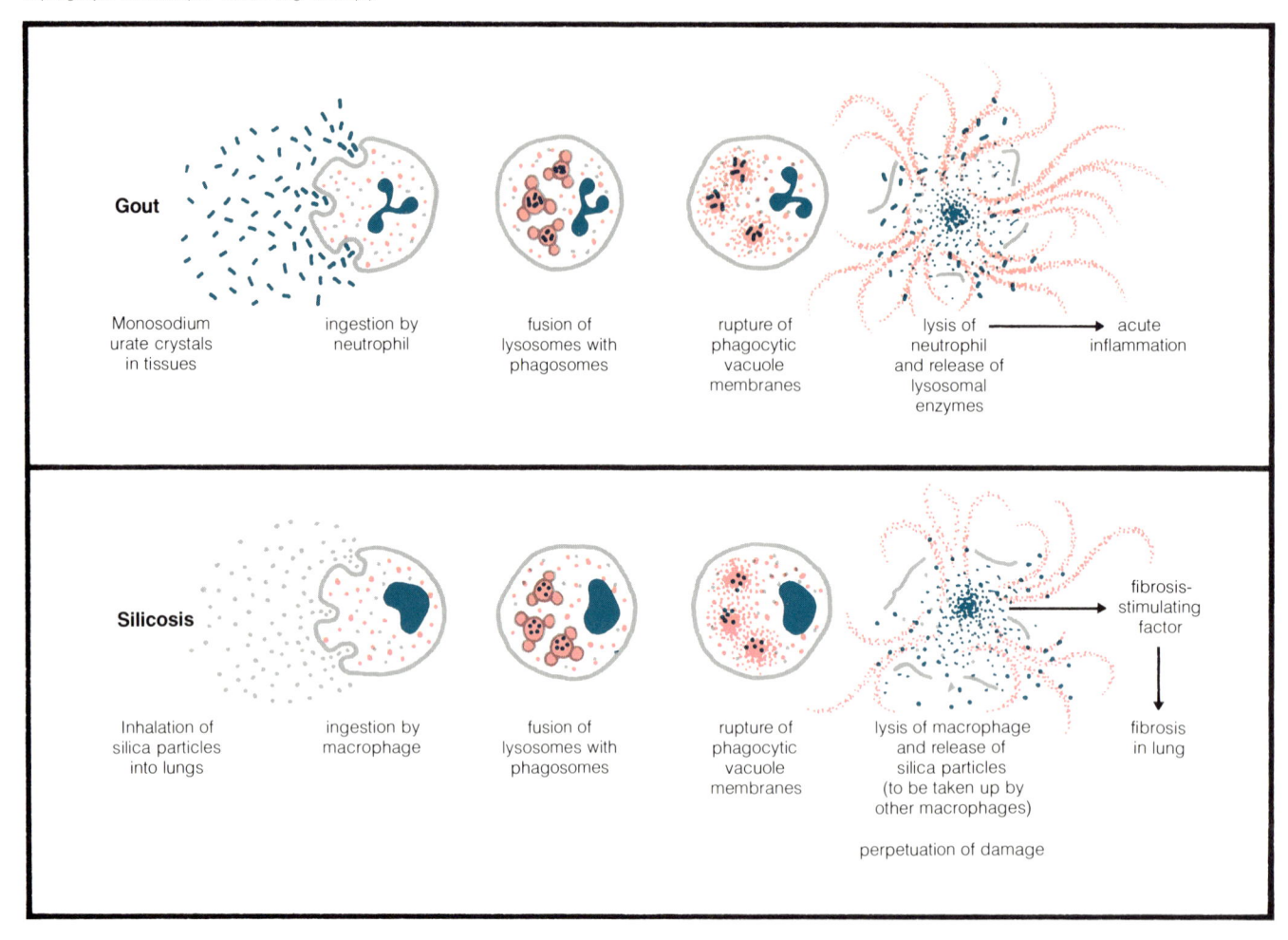

Gout

Monosodium urate crystals in tissues → ingestion by neutrophil → fusion of lysosomes with phagosomes → rupture of phagocytic vacuole membranes → lysis of neutrophil and release of lysosomal enzymes → acute inflammation

Silicosis

Inhalation of silica particles into lungs → ingestion by macrophage → fusion of lysosomes with phagosomes → rupture of phagocytic vacuole membranes → lysis of macrophage and release of silica particles (to be taken up by other macrophages) → fibrosis-stimulating factor → fibrosis in lung

perpetuation of damage

---

to release of lysosomal components. The lysosomal components worsen the inflammation either directly or by causing tissue damage (including damage to blood vessels with thrombosis and hemorrhage). The importance of neutrophil products in this response is confirmed by the fact that the reaction (erythema and edema) can be blocked if neutrophils are not present (if the animals are treated with nitrogen mustard or with specific anti-neutrophil sera). It has been postulated that an Arthus-type reaction may explain the disease called "Farmer's Lung" in which severe respiratory difficulties develop within 6 to 8 hours of inhaling dust from moldy hay.

Release of Lysosomal Products From Cells — There appear to be two major mechanisms:

1) *Cytotoxic release occurring during cell death* — This can occur with direct toxic damage to the cell's outer membrane. However, a more interesting mechanism is the "internal perforation" of the phagocytic vacuole (and intracellular release of lysosomal enzymes) that occurs when neutrophils or macrophages ingest certain kinds of particles. The best-known examples of this "suicide bag" concept are gout and silicosis (Figure 69).

In *gout*, there is a metabolic abnormality that results in the deposition of monosodium urate crystals in tissues around joints. Neutrophils phagocytize the crystals, lysosomes fuse with the phagosomes, and the monosodium urate crystals then rupture the phagocytic vacuole membrane "from within" (possibly through a hydrogen-bonding reaction). This allows lysosomal enzymes to spill into the cytoplasm, killing the cell. The enzymes spill out into the tissues inducing an acute inflammatory response. Colchicine has been used for years in the symptomatic treatment of gout; its mode of action is uncertain, but it may impair the fusion of lysosomes with the phagosome (perhaps by an effect on microtubules).

In *silicosis* there is an essentially similar series of events following the ingestion of silica particles by macrophages in the lung. In silicosis, however, two additional features are worth noting: first, there is perpetuation of the lesion because silica particles that are released as the macrophages die are soon taken up by other macrophages; and second, the disintegrating macrophages apparently release a factor that provokes fibroblastic proliferation. This probably explains the dense fibrosis that develops in silicotic lesions.

2) *"Secretory release," occurring during phagocytosis by the cell* — Unlike cytotoxic release, this is not accompanied by release of extralysosomal cytoplasmic enzymes. Here again, intracellular cyclic AMP levels are important in regulating release; increased cyclic AMP levels suppress leakage. Recently, a "lysosomal enzyme-releasing factor" (possibly C5 fragments) has been found in human serum after appropriate triggering of the complement system. Rather surprisingly this factor stimulates release of lysosomal components in the absence of phagocytizable particles.

d) Lymphocyte Products In cell-mediated immune reactions, the antigen triggers sensitized T ("thymus-dependent") lymphocytes to release an array of mediators sometimes called *lymphokines*. Such reactions are responsible for certain kinds of immunity, but they can also cause tissue damage as seen in certain infections and in transplant rejection. The prototype of cell-mediated immunity is the Mantoux test in which "tuberculin" (derived from tubercle bacilli) is injected into the skin. A positive reaction is characterized by local erythema and induration occurring maximally at 24 to 48 hours. Such a response indicates a state of "hypersensitivity" due to a previous tuberculous infection (clinically recognized or not). Histologically, the lesions show a predominantly mononuclear cell infiltrate consisting of lymphocytes and mononuclear phagocytes. These features can be attributed to the effects of lymphokines (Figure 70).

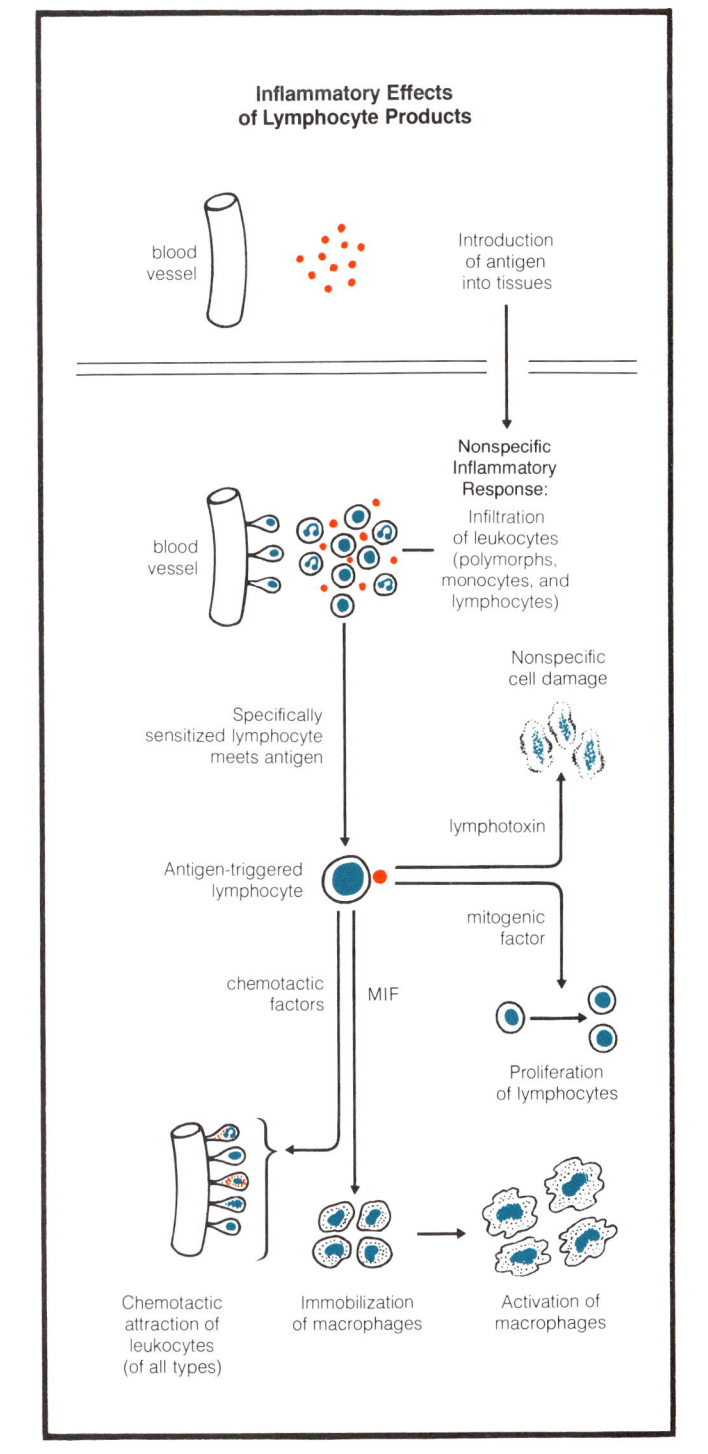

Figure 70. Inflammatory effects of lymphocyte products (lymphokines).

The lymphokines concerned in producing inflammation-related events are as follows: 1) *Migration inhibitory factor (MIF)* – This has been the most intensively studied of all the lymphocyte-derived mediators. It inhibits the migration of macrophages and thereby presumably acts to retain emigrated monocytes in the area. It also acts as a "macrophage activating factor," causing macrophages to spread their bodies out and show greater membrane ruffling, more lysosomes, better phagocytic ability, and increased glucose oxidation. These effects are obviously important in antimicrobial immunity. 2) *Chemotactic factors* – Lymphocyte-derived chemotactic factors specific for macrophages, neutrophils or basophils have been described (using the Boyden assay system). A chemotactic factor for eosinophils has also been detected when culture fluid from antigen-stimulated lymphocytes is incubated with specific antigen-antibody complexes. In addition, it has recently been claimed that lymphokines can attract lymphocytes. 3) *Lymphotoxin* – This lymphocyte-derived product is nonspecifically toxic to other cells. 4) *Skin reactive factors* – Supernatants from stimulated lymphocytes provoke delayed hypersensitivity-type reactions when injected into the skin of normal guinea pigs. These supernatants cause erythema, induration, and mononuclear cell infiltration after a delay of several hours. The responsible factors (called "skin reactive factors") have not been precisely identified. 5) *Mitogenic factor* – This factor induces proliferation of unsensitized lymphocytes in the area.

Other lymphokines that may have a role in inflammation include a factor that triggers leukocytes to release endogenous pyrogen and another one that has "colony-stimulating factor" activity, and is perhaps involved in granulopoiesis.

Another lymphocyte-derived product is the so-called *lymph node permeability factor* (LNPF). This was first isolated as an extract from lymph node cells, but similar activity was later found in extracts of nonlymphoid tissues. It induces increased vascular permeability, leukocytic infiltration, and the deposition of "fibrinoid" (fibrin-like) material at the site of injection. It is not a lymphokine because its release from lymphocytes is antigen-independent. The nature of LNPF and its significance as a mediator are not clear.

e) Other Tissue-Derived Mediators These are the factors that do not readily fit into the above groups. They include the following: 1) *Endogenous pyrogens* are fever-inducing agents released from leukocytes (described in the Systemic Effects of Inflammation). 2) *Factors involved in leukocytosis* include "neutrophil-releasing factors," "colony-stimulating factor," and "granulocytic chalone" (described in the Systemic Effects of Inflammation). 3) *Substance P* is a peptide consisting of 11 amino acids found originally by von Euler and Gaddum in 1931 in extracts of brain and intestine. It is a potent promoter of vascular permeability. 4) *Neurotensin* is another peptide consisting of 13 amino acids recently isolated from bovine hypothalamus. It induces vasodilatation and hypotension if injected intravenously. If injected locally, it causes an immediate flare and vascular leakage. 5) *Collagen fragments,* produced by the action of fibroblast-derived collagenase, have been claimed to have chemotactic activity for neutrophils. 6) *Cyclic AMP* has been reported to exert a chemotactic effect on neutrophils (when tested in the Boyden system, or in slide-coverslip preparations).

Figure 71.

Mediators Which Induce Vascular Leakage

Origin	Mediators
Plasma	kinins (bradykinin)
	anaphylatoxins (C3a, C5a) (mainly causing histamine release)
	fibrinopeptides
Tissues	vasoactive amines (histamine, 5-HT)
	slow reacting substance of anaphylaxis (SRS-A)
	prostaglandins (PGE$_1$, PGE$_2$)
	neutrophil lysosomal cationic proteins
	lymphocyte-derived "skin reactive factors"
	lymph node permeability factor (LNPF)
	substance P
	neurotensin

Role of Epinephrine or Norepinephrine in Inflammation Spector and Willoughby have proposed that these hormones might act normally as antipermeability agents and that they are somehow inactivated during inflammation. This theory was suggested by a series of experiments in which inflammatory edema was suppressed by the administration of epinephrine or norepinephrine, or their precursors (dopa, dopamine), or by treatment with inhibitors of monoamine oxidase (which destroys the hormones). This is an interesting but very speculative idea.

The Role of Mediators in Inflammatory Responses
We have presented you with a bewildering array of potential inflammatory mediators (Figures 71, 72). Which of them are important and really working to cause vascular leakage and leukocytic infiltration? A satisfactory answer is not yet available. We are faced with a variety of problems. For instance, when we inject a permeability-inducing agent we see a rapidly transient response. With this in mind, how do we explain the persistent permeability that is usual in inflammation? One explanation could be a continued production of the responsible mediator. However, with certain important mediators (like histamine), the vessels are thought to become refractory to the mediator for up to several hours after the phase of leakage. An alternative explanation is that different mediators are involved at different stages of the response. For example, it has been proposed that vasoactive amines are active in the early stages and that kinins and prostaglandins take over in later stages. Yet another explanation is that sustained leakage results from direct injury to the small vessels.

It is obvious that we have a long way to go before we can definitely attribute a particular inflammatory event to a particular mediator. Nevertheless, let us try to list the most likely candidates for significant inflammatory mediators. If we exclude exogenous factors (such as increased permeability resulting from direct vascular injury or leukocytic infiltration due to chemotactic bacterial products), then inflammation is probably mediated as follows (Figure 73): 1) Vascular leakage is caused mainly by vasoactive amines (particularly histamine), kinins (bradykinin), and/or prostaglandins. 2) Leukocytic infiltration is caused mainly by the chemotactic by-products of the complement system (especially C5

Figure 72.

Mediators Potentially Responsible for Chemotaxis of Leukocytes

Leukocyte	Chemotactic Factor

Neutrophil	bacterial and viral products
	complement system by-products
	    C5 fragments
	    C3 fragments
	    complex C$\overline{567}$
	kallikrein
	plasminogen activator
	fibrinopeptides
	fibrin degradation products
	prostaglandins (PGE$_1$)
	neutrophil-derived factors
	lymphocyte product
	collagen fragments
	cyclic AMP

Mononuclear phagocyte	bacterial products
	complement system by-products
	    C5 fragments
	    C3 fragments
	kallikrein
	plasminogen activator
	Mycobacterium tuberculosis-treated serum
	neutrophil lysosomal cationic protein
	lymphocyte product

Eosinophil	bacterial products
	complement system by-products
	    C5 fragments
	    C3 fragments
	    complex C$\overline{567}$
	eosinophil chemotactic factor of anaphylaxis (ECF-A)
	lymphocyte product

Basophil	complement system by-products C5 fragments kallikrein lymphocyte product
Lymphocyte	lymphocyte product

Chronic Inflammation

Figure 73.

> **Summary of the Most Important Endogenous Mediators of Inflammation**
>
> **Increased Vascular Permeability**
> vasoactive amines (histamine)
> kinins (bradykinin)
> prostaglandins
>
> **Leukocytic Infiltration (Chemotaxis)**
> *Neutrophils:*
> complement system by-products (C5 fragments)
> *Mononuclear phagocytes:*
> complement system by-products (C5 fragments)
> neutrophil lysosomal cationic protein
> *Eosinophils:*
> complement system by-products (C5 fragments)
> eosinophil chemotactic factor of anaphylaxis (ECF-A)
>
> **Tissue Damage**
> Neutrophil lysosomal products (*neutral* proteases)

fragments), neutrophil lysosomal cationic protein for mononuclear phagocytes, and eosinophil chemotactic factor of anaphylaxis (ECF-A) for eosinophils. 3) Tissue damage is due mainly to neutrophil lysosomal products (especially the neutral proteases).

Finally, there is an intriguing question: Why does the acute inflammatory reaction ever come to an end? With the many built-in cascade systems, one could easily envisage a self-perpetuating response. However, the enzymes involved are potentially unstable. There may be consumption of substrate, or perhaps the lymph flow carries away the mediators faster than they can be produced. In any event, it is perfectly obvious that the acute inflammatory response is self-limited.

What happens at this point? The problem is broader than inflammation, because it involves healing of the original injury as well as removal of the inflammatory products. For the time being, it is important to realize that the acute inflammatory response can cease and disappear without trace. At the other end of the spectrum, if the stimulus persists, it can blend into a new phase called *chronic inflammation.*

Chronic means long-lasting. There is, of course, no sharp limit of time between acute and chronic inflammation, but in practice the clinical course of inflammation is termed *acute* if it lasts a matter of hours or days; *chronic* if it lasts weeks, months, or years. Although the acute and chronic processes are closely related, there are many clinical as well as biologic reasons for distinguishing between them.

Chronic inflammation can arise, basically, under two different sets of circumstances:

Evolution from acute to chronic – This happens characteristically in certain infections. The basic reason is that the agent (which is capable of inducing acute inflammation) persists, so that the reaction also persists. A good example is staphylococcal infection of bone. There is at first the typical flare-up of acute inflammation; in the meantime a mass of bone is killed by the bacteria. The bacteria use this necrotic bone as a "hideout," and it becomes very difficult for the bodily defenses to reach them. So the battle continues to rage, and it may do so for several years. However, *the tissue reaction also takes on two new facets* (this is very important): *a)* the connective tissue, which is the battleground, reacts by producing more connective tissue – of a variety known as *granulation tissue* (Figure 74); and *b)* even if the exudation of neutrophils continues, there is a great local increase in mononuclear cells of various kinds – macrophages, lymphocytes, plasma cells (Figure 75). Under the microscope these two main qualitative differences are so striking that you can recognize a focus as "chronic" at a glance.

Chronic inflammation without any acute phase – Many injurious agents act in this manner. They persist in the tissues and induce a cellular reaction of the chronic type, without a significant acute phase. Typical examples can be found among bacteria (the tubercle bacillus) and chemical agents (fats and oils, sterile foreign bodies). There are certain conditions that are obviously chronic inflammatory diseases (as judged histologically), although the causative agent is not visible and remains a mystery; a typical example is sarcoidosis.

Histologically, the two main features of chronic inflammation are the presence of granulation tissue and the mononuclear predominance. *Granulation tissue* is a term borrowed from the terminology of wound healing (where it represents the young connective tissue that

Figure 74. Typical granulation tissue lining the bottom of a wound (amputation stump). Note the newly formed capillaries rising toward the surface (marked by fibrin, at top), a giant cell containing a foreign body (lower left), and round spaces that represent fat liberated from necrotic adipose tissue.

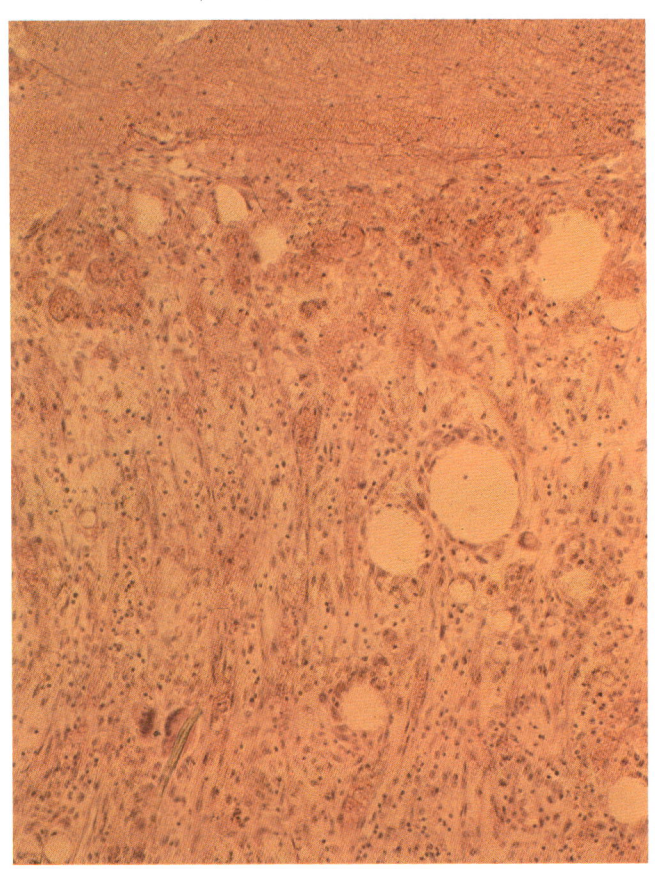

Figure 75. Predominance of mononuclear cells in a typical chronic inflammatory infiltrate in two tissues: kidney (top), and breast (bottom).

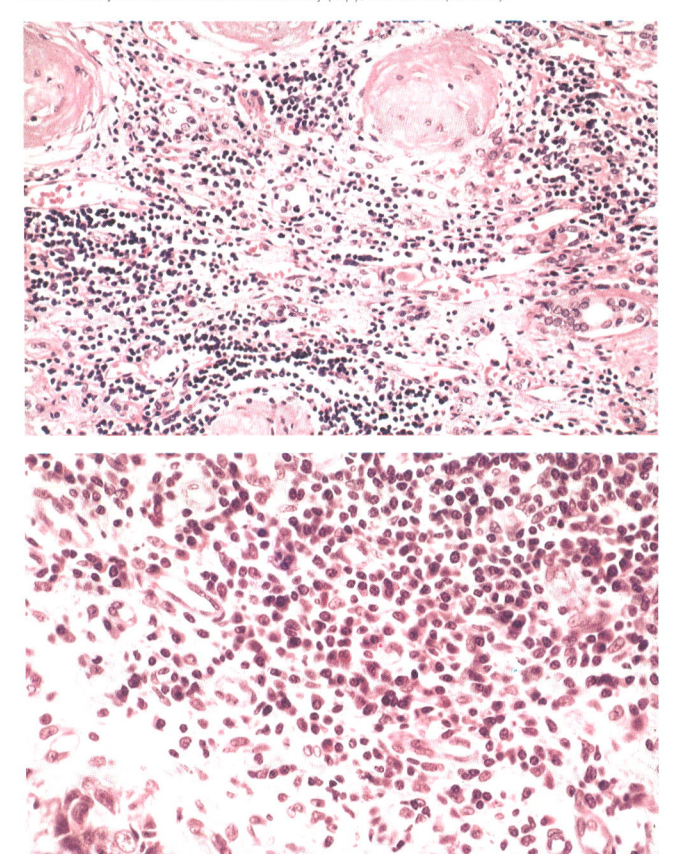

lines or fills a gaping wound). Compared with ordinary loose connective tissue, it is more cellular. Its cellular population includes neutrophils, other "inflammatory" cells, and fibroblasts. It is also more vascular; its newly forming capillaries are lined by poorly joined endothelial cells, and are therefore leaky (Figure 76). As to its biologic significance, granulation tissue is a response of the connective tissue cells and vessels to the irritant.

As to the *mononuclear predominance*, we have already noticed its beginnings in the latter phases of acute inflammation, where the proportion of mononuclear phagocytes (or macrophages) began to rise. In certain forms of chronic inflammation, other cell types appear besides the macrophages: lymphocytes, plasma cells, eosinophils; their presence will suggest to you that these are, in part, immunologic reactions. The bacteria that are capable of inducing chronic inflammation also elicit an immune response (and the cells that are concerned with it are, of course, primarily mononuclear cells). In other cases, the injurious agent is not antigenic, but calls for extensive phagocytosis (think of an oily injection, or of a suture thread). In this condition the mononuclear cells will be only, or almost only, macrophages.

Another biologic feature of chronic inflammation is the low-key role of vascular events; there is much less vasodilatation and usually less exudation. Clinically, this means less redness and less heat. This explains why the tuberculous abscess also goes under the name of "cold abscess."

Forms of Chronic Inflammation

Depending on the predominance of one or another feature of the reaction, several histologic and clinical varieties can be described. The first three can probably be

Figure 76. The leakiness of newly formed capillaries in granulation tissue is demonstrated by a red blood cell that is slipping out between two endothelial cells.

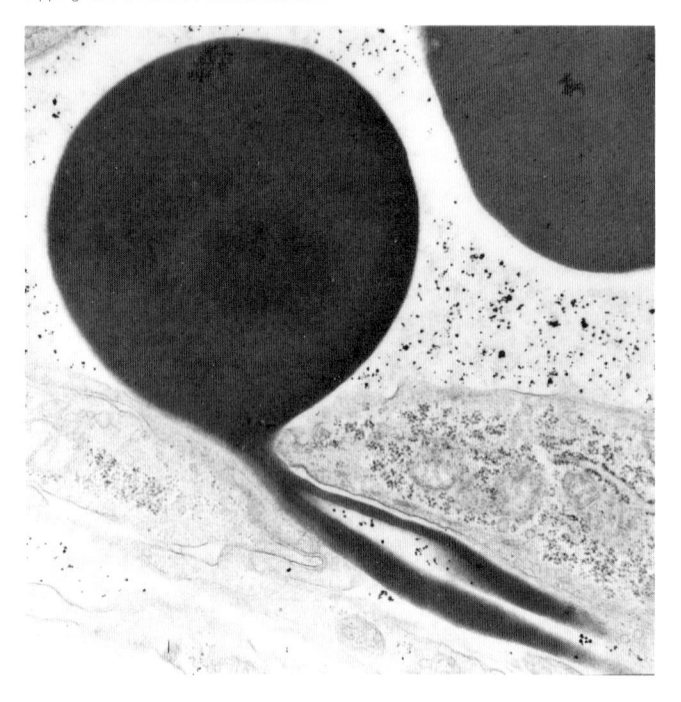

predicted on the basis of what you already know; the fourth is rather special.

1) *Chronic fibrous inflammation* – The main feature is the production of abundant fibrous tissue. Fibrous tissue tends to contract (by a mechanism that we shall discuss later) and the result may be a mechanical defect, such as a stiffened joint, stenosis of a duct, etc.

2) *Chronic serous inflammation* – The principal feature is a slow accumulation of clear exudate, resembling serum, either in a serous cavity or in a joint. It occurs at times when a serous membrane or a synovial membrane is chronically inflamed. Tuberculous infection of the pleura offers a typical example.

3) *Chronic suppurative inflammation (abscess)* – An abscess is an *accumulation of pus in a newly formed cavity*. Students are often confused about abscesses. Are they acute or chronic lesions? This depends on the size. A microscopic or semi-microscopic abscess (such as a pimple) can easily form in a day or two and is, therefore, "acute." A large abscess that would require surgical drainage takes days and weeks to form and is more properly considered a chronic lesion, although polymorphs continue to pour into it. The wall of the abscess, which exudes the pus, has long been known as the *pyogenic membrane*. Its structure is typically that of granulation tissue, more cellular on the inside, more fibrous on the outside. The hollow that fills with pus is formed by necrosis and liquefaction of a mass of tissue. This necrosis is usually brought about by pyogenic bacteria and its liquefaction is caused by the lysosomal enzymes contained in the neutrophils.

It is of great practical importance to know the possible evolutions of an abscess (Figure 77). In the best circumstances, the bacteria are killed off; the pus is then slowly reabsorbed by the macrophages of the pyogenic membrane, while the spherical wall itself slowly "clamps down" on the contents, as the granulation tissue shrinks. Ultimately there will remain a fibrous scar containing blood pigments and possibly some calcified remnants of necrotic material. If they are not drained surgically, abscesses often drain spontaneously either through the skin or into a hollow organ (the latter course may lead to further complications). One question arises: What are the forces that lead an abscess to try to work its way toward a surface and void its contents, as if it "knew" how to heal itself? Several mechanisms are at work. First, the abscess has to grow. This occurs either because virulent bacteria spread beyond its capsule and a new capsule forms beyond them, or because the bacteria kill off the internal layers of the lining while extra layers are built up outside. In so growing, the abscess follows the path of least resistance. It will follow fascial planes and tend to spare the striated muscles. When the abscess bulges beneath the skin or a mucosa, it stretches it until the overlying tissue becomes necrotic (either from the effect of bacterial action or ischemia), and the abscess bursts open or is evacuated surgically. Its healing is thereby greatly accelerated.

4) *Chronic granulomatous inflammation* – This is perhaps the commonest variety of chronic inflammation. The term "granulomatous" arose because the affected tissues contain multiple, small, grain-like structures called "granulomas." Granulomas can be microscopic or up to about 1 mm in diameter; they are aggregates of inflammatory cells, usually arranged concentrically around the causal agent (not always visible). The significance of the granuloma is that it represents a local reaction to a small amount, or "quantum" of an irritating agent. Many (but

Figure 77. The natural history of an abscess.

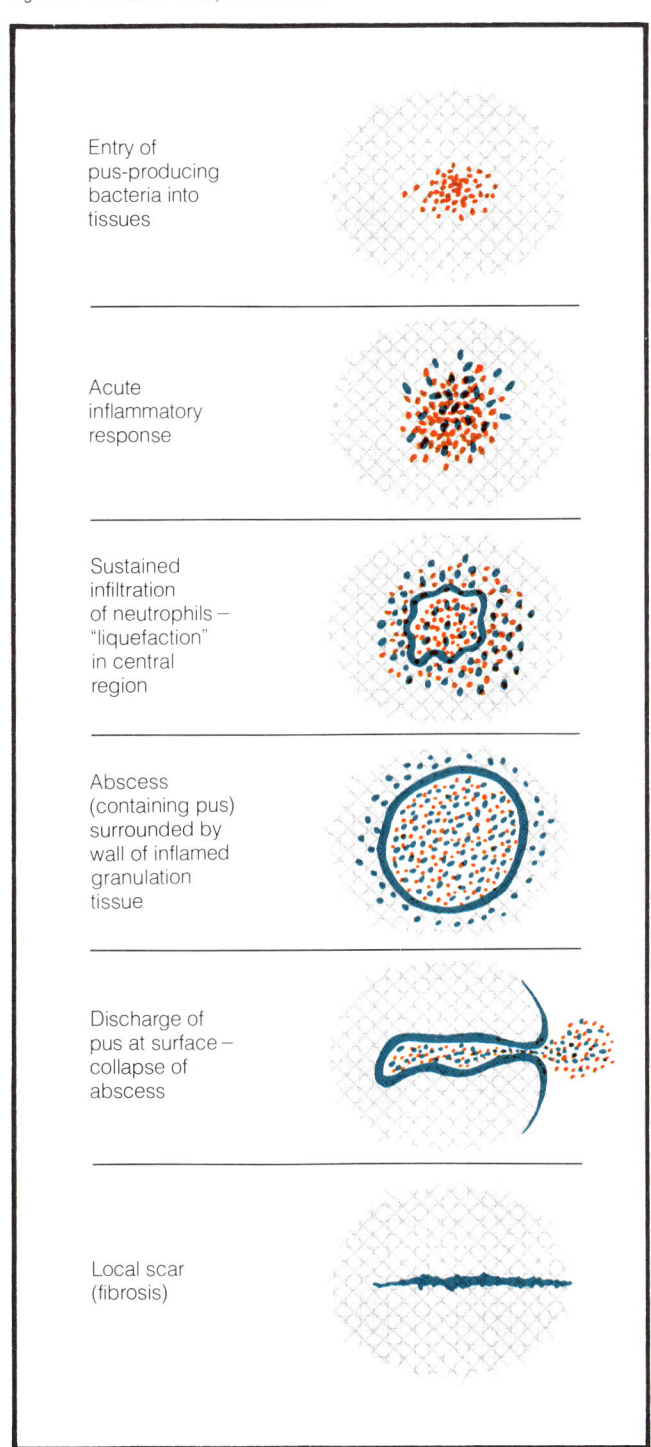

Entry of pus-producing bacteria into tissues

Acute inflammatory response

Sustained infiltration of neutrophils – "liquefaction" in central region

Abscess (containing pus) surrounded by wall of inflamed granulation tissue

Discharge of pus at surface – collapse of abscess

Local scar (fibrosis)

Figure 78. Typical tubercle in a human lung.

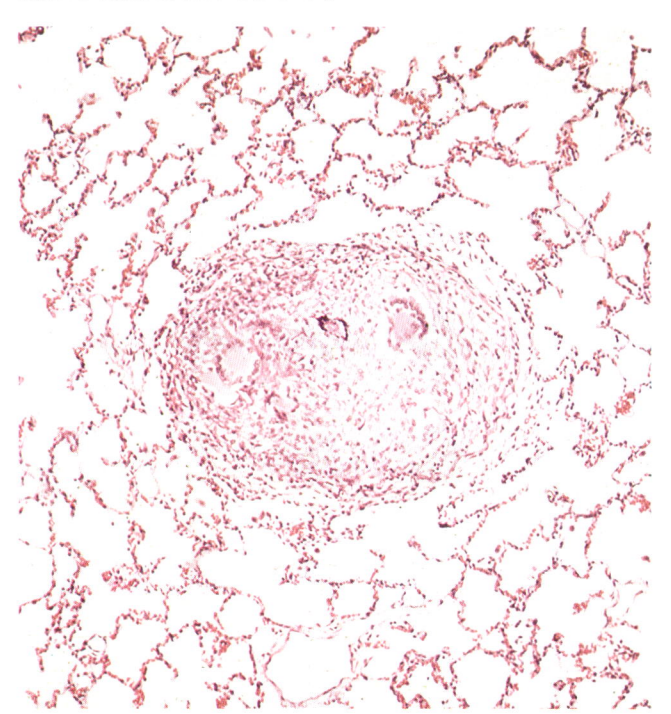

not all) granulomas represent an immune reaction to this agent, at least to some extent. The most common causes are: *a*) certain bacterial infections: typical examples are tuberculosis, leprosy, syphilis; *b*) fungal and parasitic infections, such as histoplasmosis, schistosomiasis; *c*) aseptic foreign bodies, like suture threads, asbestos, talcum powder (once used for surgical gloves); *d*) unknown: for example, sarcoidosis.

Granulomas due to different agents are not all exactly alike. Let us examine as a prototype the granuloma of tuberculosis (usually known as a "tubercle") in which the concentric arrangement is most obvious (Figure 78). Its components are the following:

1) *Macrophages* – The major element of a tubercle is a large, aggregated mass of macrophages. Histologically, these macrophages are big cells with pale pink cytoplasm, with an appearance vaguely resembling epithelium – hence they are commonly called "epithelioid cells". Many of these cells contain living *Mycobacterium tuberculosis* organisms. Curiously, however, macrophages seem to lose their ability to show active phagocytosis after their transformation into epithelioid cells.

Figure 79. Foreign body giant cells. *Top:* Cross section through a surgical suture several weeks after it has been inserted. Note the many giant cells (H & E). *Bottom:* The same field viewed by polarized light: the birefringent filaments of the suture stand out much more clearly.

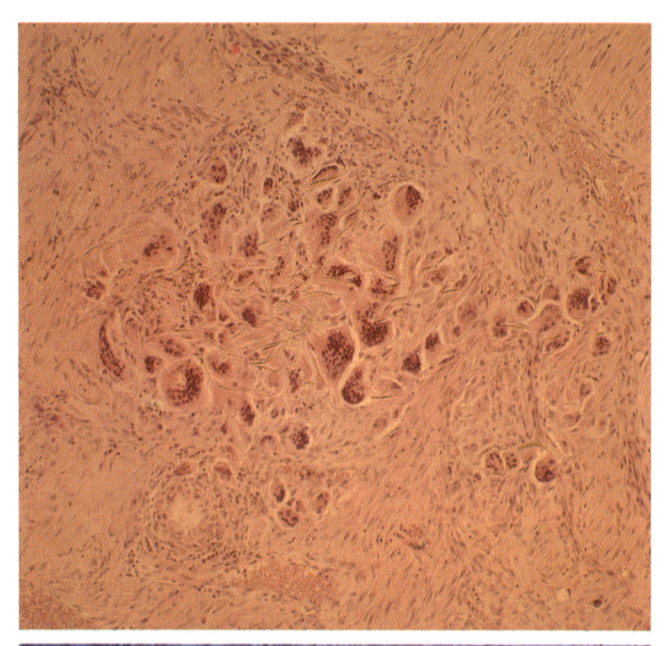

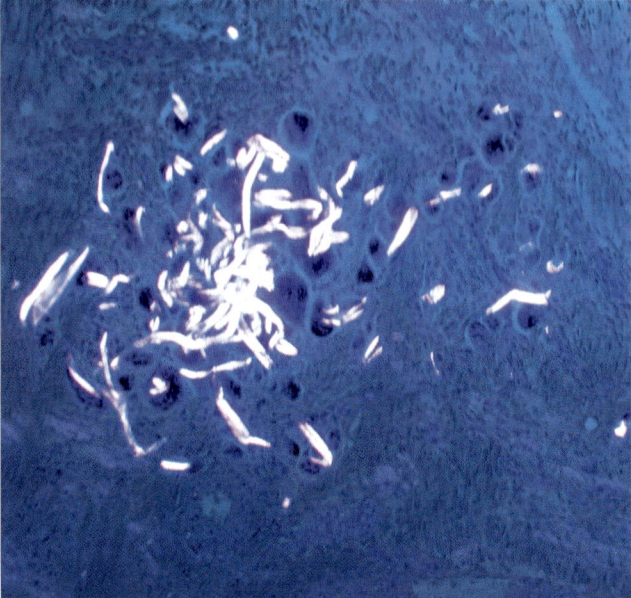

2) *Caseous necrosis* – In a fully developed tubercle, the central part of the mass of epithelioid cells dies, possibly as a result of a cell-mediated immune reaction. These dead areas are usually cheese-like in appearance and consistency, hence the term "caseous necrosis."

3) *Giant cells* – Scattered amongst the epithelioid cells are large "giant cells" that contain multiple nuclei. These cells arise primarily by fusion of macrophages (although it is also possible that nuclear division can occur secondarily after the giant cell has formed). Medical students are usually taught that the giant cells in a tubercle have nuclei which are arranged in a ring around the outer part of the cytoplasm – the so-called Langhans' giant cell. This arrangement is said to contrast with the central clustering of nuclei found in the so-called foreign body giant cell typically found around extraneous materials (Figure 79). However, such a distinction between giant cells in different types of lesions is not valid; both types can be found in all kinds of granulomatous responses. In any case, the significance of this nuclear pattern is not clear. Spector's group has recently reported that in experimental granulomas, Langhans' giant cells convert into foreign body cells during treatment with colchicine (a drug which, among other effects, disrupts microtubules).

4) *Lymphocytes* – Lymphocytes usually accumulate in fairly large numbers around the outside of the main mass of epithelioid cells.

5) *Fibrosis* – Also outside the epithelioid cell mass is a zone of fibrosis. This is an area in which fibroblasts progressively lay down collagen, thus forming scar tissue. Continuing fibrosis can be a serious consequence of chronic inflammation, particularly if it is so placed that it distorts or occludes the lumen of any tube or duct within the body.

Incidentally, it is worth noting that the central, epithelioid region of a granuloma contains no blood vessels. This is in striking contrast to granulation tissue (in areas of healing) which contains enormous numbers of new blood vessels.

How do other granulomas differ from tubercles? The major elements are the same: There are macrophages, giant cells, lymphocytes, and fibrosis. However, certain differences are found in response to different causes. For example, caseous necrosis is not found in sarcoidosis or

Figure 80. (top) Autoradiograph of macrophages and giant cells stuck to glass coverslip (inserted subcutaneously in a rat). Note silver grains over five nuclei, indicating that these cells had incorporated tritiated thymidine into their DNA (hence that they were preparing to divide).

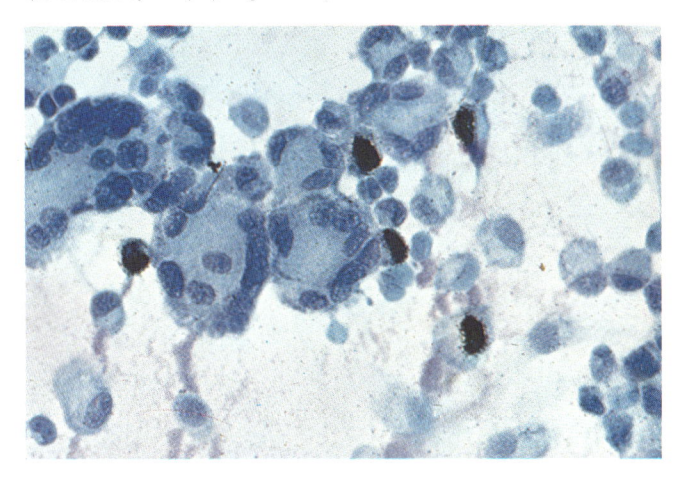

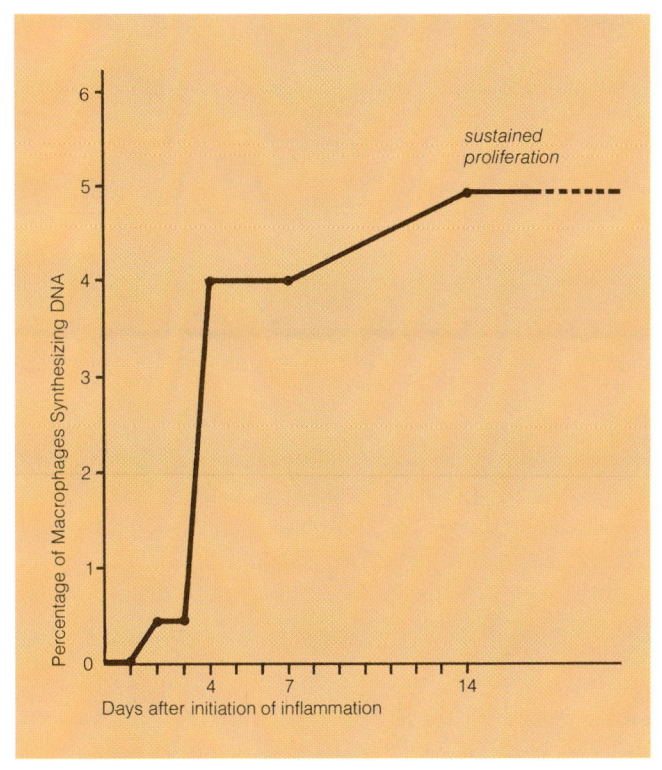

Figure 81. (bottom) Proliferation of macrophages in chronic inflammation.

foreign body reactions. Certain kinds of lesions may contain a more varied array of cell types, including plasma cells and eosinophils. In addition, fibrosis may be either more or less prominent in different circumstances.

The kinetics of macrophages in chronic inflammatory lesions. Where do the macrophages come from and what happens to them? Metchnikoff believed that macrophages were derived from lymphocytes, and this view was popular for many years. Recently, however, it has become established that the major precursor of the inflammatory macrophage is the blood monocyte. Volkman and Gowans injected rats with tritiated thymidine, thus labelling all dividing precursors of monocytes in the bone marrow. The tritiated thymidine is incorporated into new DNA by cells preparing to divide; the radioactive tritium can be detected in the nucleus of labelled cells by means of autoradiography (Figure 80). After several hours, labelled monocytes were detected in the blood and could then be traced as they emigrated from the blood into inflamed tissues. In these experiments, the labelled inflammatory "macrophages" attached themselves to glass coverslips that had been placed over skin abrasions or inside subcutaneous pockets. Volkman and Gowans proved that these macrophages came from bone marrow-derived cells (that is, from monocytes rather than from lymphocytes) by the following procedure: They destroyed the bone marrow by x-ray and thereby prevented the appearance of macrophages on the coverslips. However, macrophages did not appear on coverslips if the experimental animals were injected intravenously with a suspension of labelled bone marrow cells from another animal (a suspension of lymphocytes was ineffective).

At one time it was believed that monocytes did not divide after they entered the tissues and became macrophages, but this has recently been shown to be incorrect. Ryan and Spector implanted glass coverslips subcutaneously into rats and mice, and then at various stages injected the animals with tritiated thymidine. One hour after injection, the coverslips were removed and the adherent macrophages were examined by autoradiography. As shown in Figure 81, no significant labelling was found for the first three days after implantation of the coverslip, but on the fourth day 4% of the macrophages were labelled (indicating the presence of premitotic DNA synthesis). This level of labelling was maintained

Figure 82. Percentages of mononuclear phagocytes showing DNA synthesis in different "compartments."

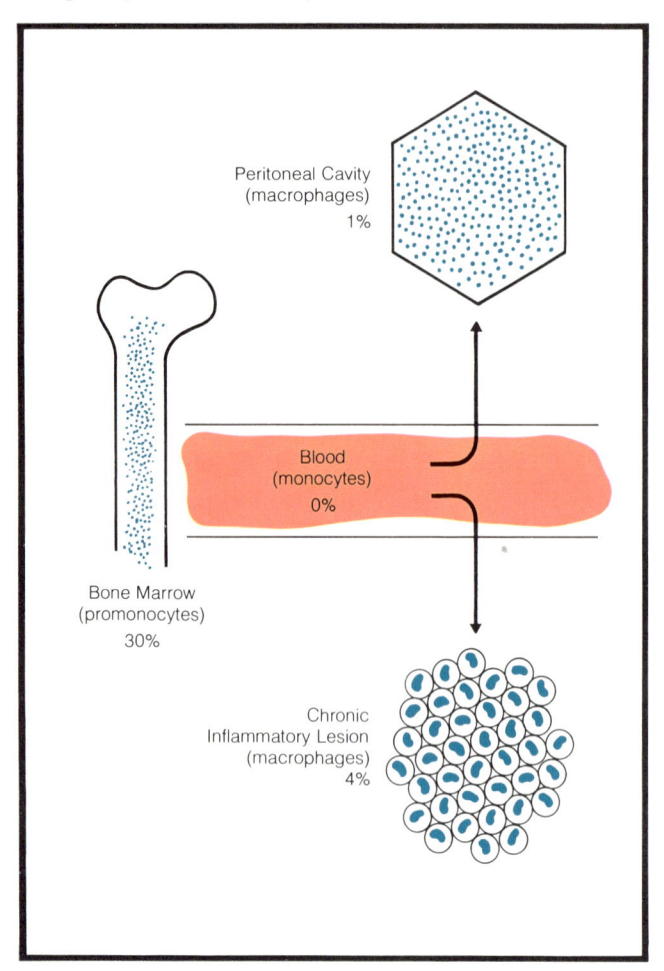

Figure 83. Macrophage kinetics in chronic inflammation.

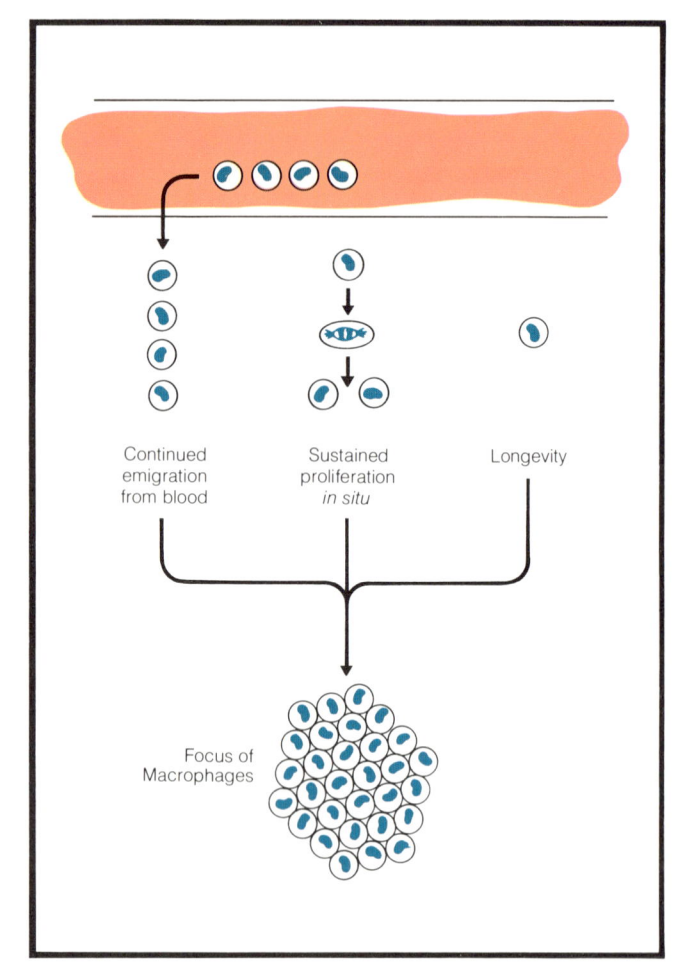

thereafter for at least six months. Incidentally, the coverslips showed many multinucleated giant cells (Figure 80). As previously mentioned, these cells arise primarily from the fusion of macrophages (although examples of synchronous nuclear labelling with tritiated thymidine, and subsequent mitoses, in such cells were not uncommon in later stages).

Let us consider the percentages of mononuclear phagocytes showing DNA synthesis at any one time (Figure 82). In the bone marrow of rats, 30% of the promonocytes are labelled following a single pulse of tritiated thymidine. No monocytes are labelled. In the peritoneal cavity, 1% of the macrophages are labelled. In inflammatory lesions, 4% of the macrophages are labelled.

This means that when monocytes leave the blood they are triggered to divide, especially in inflamed areas. The stimulus for this division is not known. An attractive idea is that a "mitogenic mediator" is present in chronic inflammatory lesions, but there is no substantive evidence for this yet.

In kinetic studies of various kinds of experimental granulomas, Ryan and Spector demonstrated that persistent infiltration of macrophages in chronic inflammation results from one or more of the following factors (Figure 83): 1) *Continued emigration of monocytes from the blood* – With certain irritants (such as B. pertussis vaccine) there is continual recruitment of new cells from the blood. 2) *Sustained proliferation of macrophages in*

64

situ — This occurs, to some extent, as long as the irritant persists in the tissues. 3) *Longevity of macrophages* — In some experimental granulomas, macrophages remain for long periods, at least for several months, without dividing or moving away.

In certain kinds of lesions, one of this trio of factors is likely to dominate, but in most cases all three probably operate to keep macrophages in the area.

Why does the irritant persist and lead to chronic inflammation? It is easy to answer this question when the irritant is clearly not degradable by the phagocytes (certain foreign particulate materials, certain bacterial products). Tuberculosis tends to persist because *Mycobacterium tuberculosis* is able to survive happily inside the macrophages, possibly because there is a failure of lysosomal fusion with phagosomes. Sometimes, as in the case of sarcoidosis, we cannot answer because we do not know the cause of the inflammatory response.

The role of immunologic factors in chronic inflammation — Kenneth Warren and his colleagues found that intravenously injected particles of bentonite, a colloidal hydrated aluminum silicate, lodged in arterioles within the lungs and elicited a modest foreign body reaction which is composed of macrophages. Similar lesions occurred in normal animals if the particles were previously coated with schistosome egg antigens or culture filtrates of either *Mycobacterium tuberculosis* or *Histoplasma capsulatum* organisms. However, if the animals had been specifically sensitized (and showed cell-mediated immunity) against the particular antigen on the particles, very large granulomas developed. From these experiments, it was proposed that cell-mediated immunity plays an important part in infective granulomatous reactions.

These studies were extended by Emil Unanue and Baruj Benacerraf, who coated polyacrylamide beads with proteins and injected them intravenously into normal or immune guinea pigs. Large granulomas developed in the lung only in the presence of carrier determinants of hapten-protein conjugates. Animals immune to DNP-hemocyanin developed large granulomas in response to beads coated with hemocyanin or DNP-hemocyanin, but not to beads coated with DNP on another unrelated antigen (Figure 84). This pattern of responsiveness is characteristic of a reaction mediated by T lymphocytes.

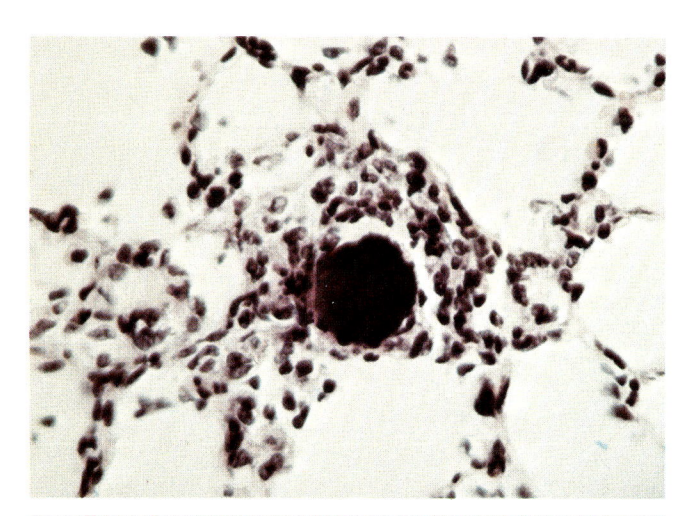

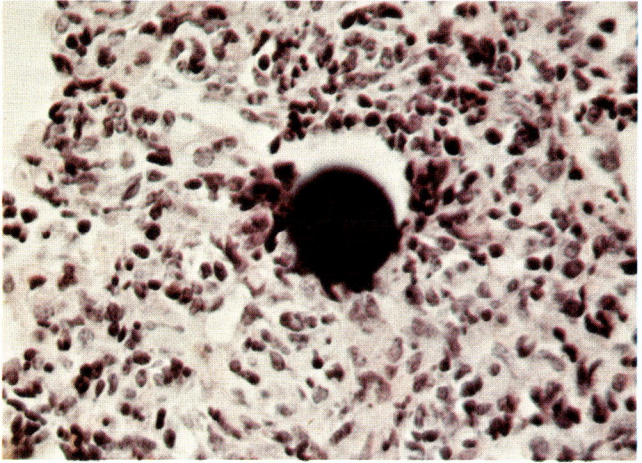

Figure 84. Reactions to polyacrylamide beads in lungs of guinea pigs immunized against DNP-hemocyanin. *Top:* Poor reaction around bead coated with DNP-BCG. *Bottom:* Large granulomatous reaction around bead coated with hemocyanin.

Systemic Effects of Inflammation

In examining a sick patient, the physician searches for signs of inflammatory disease by looking for fever (an abnormally high body temperature) and leukocytosis (an abnormally high white cell count in the blood). These two signs are the most characteristic of the generalized effects of inflammation – whether induced by infection or by damaged tissue. Another well-known change is the increased erythrocyte sedimentation rate (ESR) – the red blood cells sink to the bottom of a tube more rapidly than normal. This occurs because the red cells aggregate more readily into rouleaux, probably because of a change in plasma protein composition.

Fever

Normal body temperature is maintained at around 37°C (98°F) by a hypothalamic thermoregulatory center which senses temperature changes in the blood coming to the brain (Figure 85). With a fall in blood temperature the thermoregulatory center triggers constriction of blood vessels in the skin. The skin temperature then falls; this stimulates skin thermoreceptors which induce reflex stimulation of skeletal muscles; shivering ensues which causes heat production and thereby an increase in blood temperature. If the blood temperature rises above normal, the skin blood vessels dilate and there is sweating, each causing heat loss and a decrease in blood temperature.

How does fever occur? The studies of Barry Wood, Elisha Atkins, and their colleagues have shown that fever usually results from the release of factors called "endogenous pyrogens" into the blood. These factors are proteins that have an action on the hypothalamus similar to the effect of cold (Figure 85); they induce vasoconstriction in the skin and shivering ("chills"). This results in an inappropriate elevation of the central temperature. Eventually, though, vasodilatation and sweating usually occur, and the fever subsides (Figure 86). This change reflects a regaining of control by the thermoregulatory center, perhaps as blood pyrogen levels fall.

The sources of endogenous pyrogen – At first it was thought that endogenous pyrogen was released only from neutrophils. Later studies have shown that pyrogens can also be derived from monocytes, macrophages and probably eosinophils. Release of pyrogens occurs following exposure of the cells to various stimuli: a) phagocytosis, b) bacterial lipopolysaccharides (endo-

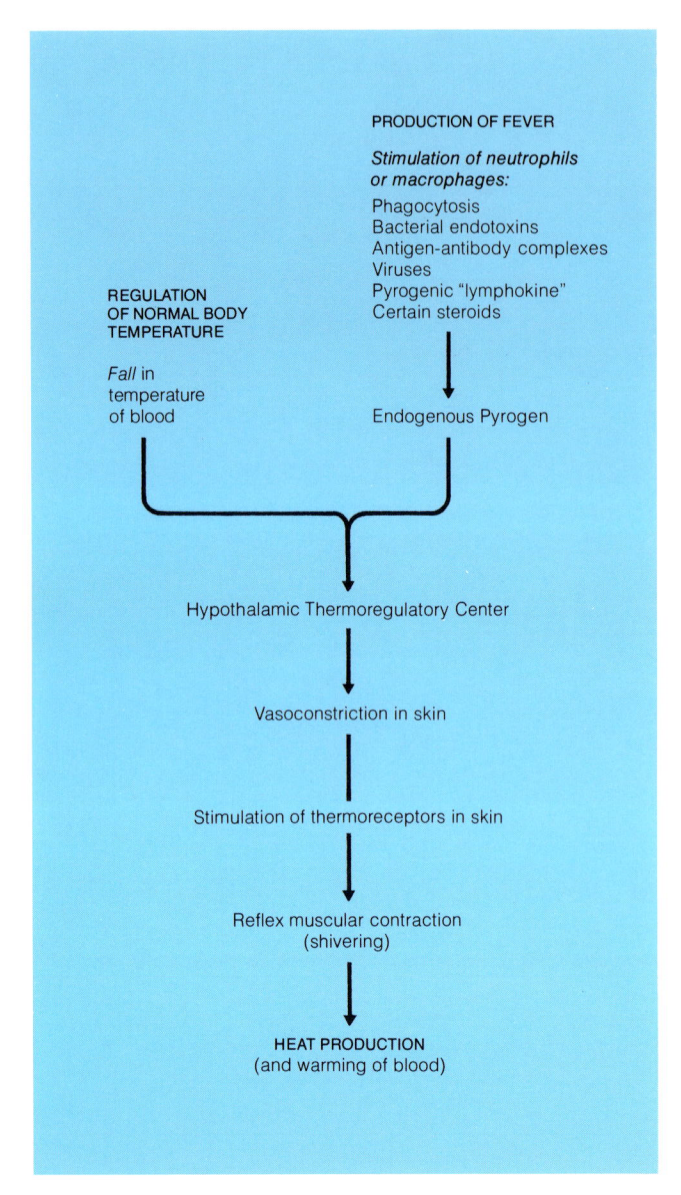

Figure 85. Regulation of normal body temperature, and the production of fever.

Figure 86. (top) Temperature chart showing a fever curve.
Figure 87. (bottom) Schema of normal neutrophil kinetics.

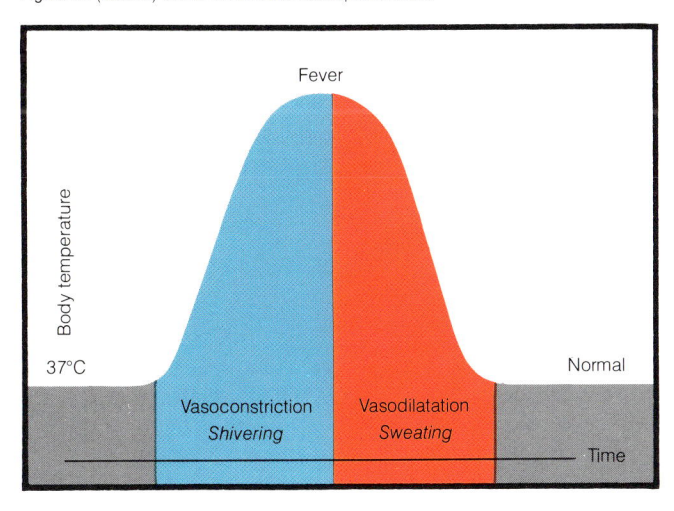

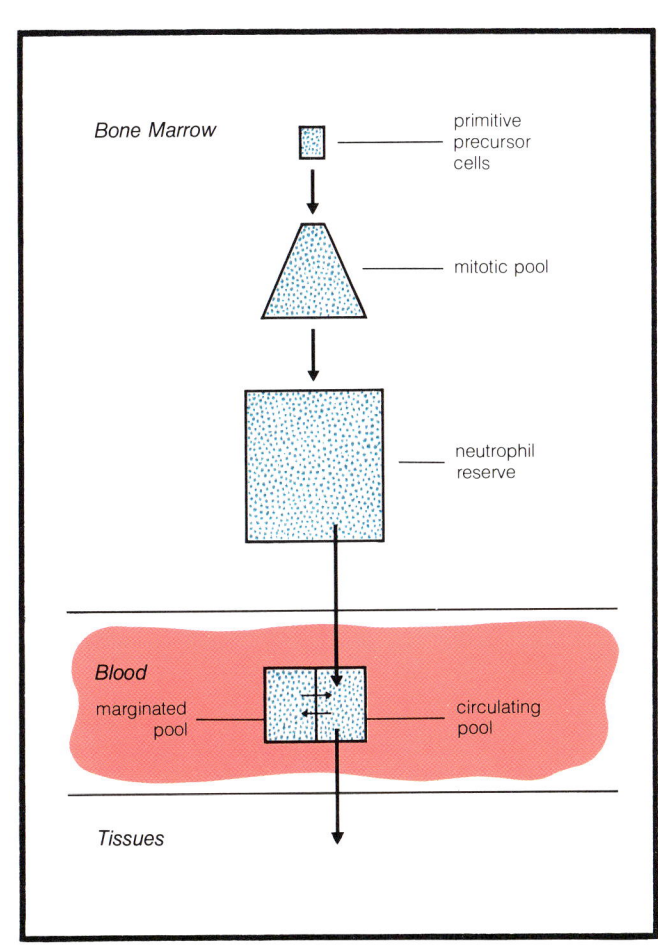

toxins), *c)* antigen-antibody complexes, *d)* certain viruses, *e)* a pyrogenic lymphokine, *f)* certain steroids (such as etiocholanolone – a metabolite of androgens), and *g)* bile acids. When the cells are appropriately stimulated, pyrogen release is detectable after two hours and continues for about twelve hours. Interestingly, corticosteroids and estrogens inhibit pyrogen release *in vitro*, helping to explain why such hormones have an antipyretic (fever-suppressing) effect *in vivo*.

How do endogenous pyrogens work? The answer is, once again, that we do not know. However, recent studies suggest that certain prostaglandins may be involved, perhaps as intermediary neurohumoral transmitters in the hypothalamus. Note that prostaglandin synthesis is inhibited by aspirin and aspirin-like drugs (traditional antipyretic agents).

Why does fever occur? Presumably fever serves some generally useful purpose in combating disease – otherwise it probably would not have survived as a mechanism. However, this "purpose" remains a mystery.

Leukocytosis

The number of leukocytes normally found in the circulating blood ranges from 4,000 to 11,000 per cubic mm. If there is a focus of acute inflammation in the body, this leukocyte count can rise to much higher levels, with almost all of the increase due to neutrophils. Sometimes an unusually high eosinophil count is found. This suggests that the patient has either an allergic-type illness or a parasitic infection. The neutrophils found in blood smears are not only more numerous, but usually are also more immature ("band forms" and metamyelocytes). This "shift to the left" (characterized by a relative lack of nuclear segmentation) occurs because increased demands are being made on the bone marrow for the production and release of neutrophils. In severe infections, the neutrophils may contain Döhle bodies (basophilic masses of rough endoplasmic reticulum), or "toxic" granules (unusually large azurophil granules), or empty vacuoles.

Normal neutrophil kinetics (Figure 87) Primitive precursor cells in the bone marrow proliferate to form a progressively expanding "mitotic pool" consisting of myeloblasts, promyelocytes, and myelocytes. After mitosis stops, the cells mature; these maturing cells make up the bone marrow's huge "neutrophil reserve" (nor-

Figure 88. (top) Factors possibly involved in leukocytosis.
Figure 89. (bottom) Schema of mechanisms of leukocytosis.

Factors Possibly Involved in Leukocytosis

Type of Effect	Factors
Release from "marginated pool" (eg, in lung)	Exercise, epinephrine
Release from bone marrow "neutrophil reserve"	"Neutrophil-releasing factors"— "leukocytosis-inducing factor" C3 fragments
Stimulation of proliferation of precursors in bone marrow	"Colony-stimulating factor"

mally containing more than ten times the total number of neutrophils present in the blood). In the blood over half of the neutrophils are normally in a "marginated pool," consisting of cells stuck to the walls of small blood vessels, particularly in the lungs. Most neutrophils stay in the circulation for about seven hours before dying or emigrating into the tissues. It has been calculated that we produce (and lose) 10^{11} neutrophils (weighing a total of about 80 grams) every day.

The causes of leukocytosis. — The mechanisms responsible for inflammatory leukocytosis have not been clearly identified. However, several factors are known to induce leukocytosis under experimental conditions (Figures 88, 89): *a*) Factors that induce *release of neutrophils from the "marginated pool"* (producing a rapid rise of *mature* neutrophils in the blood); these include exercise and epinephrine. *b*) *Neutrophil-releasing factors*

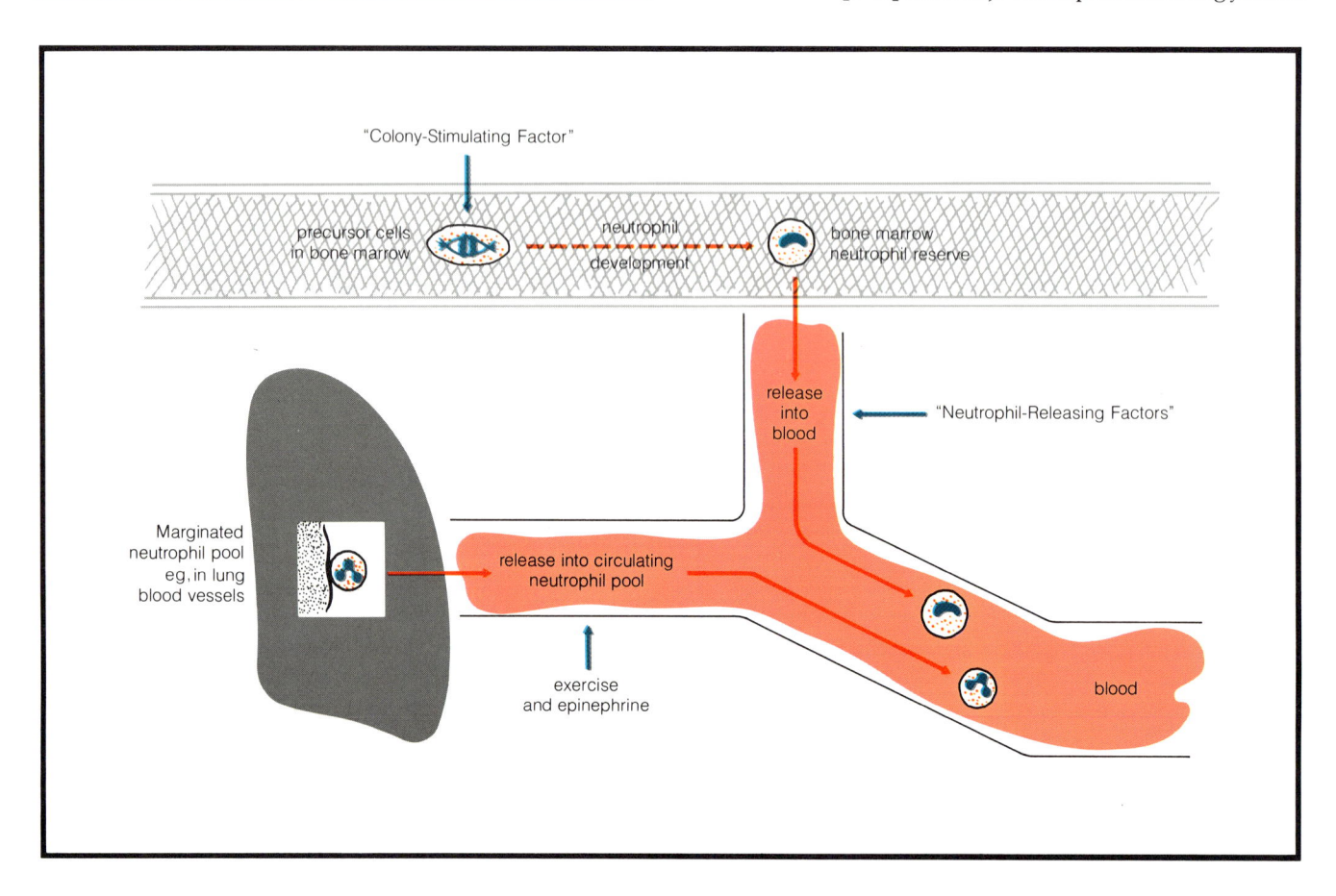

Inflammation
The Healing Phase

which induce release of neutrophils from the bone marrow's reserve and produce a transient rise of immature neutrophils in the blood within a few hours of injection. The best known is Albert Gordon's "leukocytosis-inducing factor" (LIF), detected in the plasma of animals that were injected a few hours previously with bacterial products (including endotoxin). Similar activity has been found when C3 fragments are cleaved from the third component of serum complement by $C\overline{42}$ enzyme, which may explain why certain patients with C3 deficiency fail to show leukocytosis in response to infection. *c) Factors that stimulate proliferation* of neutrophil precursors in the bone marrow and produce a slow, but relatively sustained, rise in the number of blood leukocytes (maximal at 24 to 48 hours). The most intensively studied is "colony-stimulating factor" (C-SF), so-named because it specifically stimulates the proliferation of bone marrow "colony-forming cells" (neutrophil and monocyte precursors). When bone marrow cells are suspended in semisolid agar, proliferation (to form "colonies") does not occur unless C-SF is incorporated into the culture medium. C-SF is a glycoprotein found in serum and urine, and enormously high levels are found in the blood within a few minutes of injecting endotoxin and other bacterial products. C-SF can also be extracted from salivary glands, lung, thymus, and various other tissues, but the cells that produce it have not been identified. Various cell types are probably responsible, with macrophages at the top of the list. It has recently been shown that a lymphokine has C-SF activity.

To balance the effect of C-SF, it has been proposed that the proliferation of neutrophil precursors in the bone marrow is specifically inhibited by a "granulocytic chalone," a polypeptide factor found in immature and mature neutrophils.

Why does leukocytosis occur?   There is little doubt that leukocytosis is a useful defensive reaction, geared to provide an abundant supply of cells for the inflammatory response.

The healing of a local injury calls into play two sets of biological processes; depending on the tissues involved, one or the other may prevail:

The first is *regeneration*. This is self-explanatory: it implies that lost cells are being replaced by cells of the same kind. Not all tissues are capable of this feat; in order to predict the ultimate fate of an injury you must remember the basic rules of regeneration in mammals. For example, connective tissue regenerates well except for hyaline cartilage; epithelia regenerate well, but whole parts of epithelial organs, such as nephrons, do not regenerate properly. Smooth muscle regenerates well; striated muscle could regenerate if the severed ends were perfectly juxtaposed, but in practice this is rarely accomplished.

When regeneration is not possible, replacement occurs through a process called *repair*. This is the replacement of lost tissue (of any kind) by a mass of connective tissue and ultimately by a fibrous mass called *a scar*. However, one should not think of regeneration and repair as mutually exclusive. The repair process as accomplished by connective tissue includes the cleaning-up operation, which is essential in the healing of any injury. Even in those cases in which the lost tissue can be replaced with new tissue of the same kind (like epidermis), a temporary filling of connective tissue is formed anyway: a provisional patch, as it were, which later on will be slowly reabsorbed and disappear.

The mechanisms of repair are built right into the inflammatory reaction, because they are set in motion almost simultaneously with it and build up momentum as the days go by. Its two main agents are the macrophage, which cleans up the mess, and the fibroblast, which patches up the damage. Both these cells are always at work at the periphery of an inflammatory focus, where they wall off the area even if the inflammation is still underway. A good example is the wall of an abscess, which may be just 2 mm thick: on the inner surface polymorphs may still be pouring out, whereas only 1 or 2 mm away the macrophages are removing debris, and the fibroblasts are walling off the whole area, forming the beginning of the scar. Thus it is better to speak of a *healing process* rather than of a healing phase, because the exudative and healing events can take place side by side.

Because new tissue is formed, which must be supplied with oxygen, repair is accompanied by the formation of new blood vessels. Here again, let us return to Cohnheim for a description of this process:

"The question, How does the new formation of blood-vessels take place? although it has so long engaged the attention of anatomists and pathologists, awaits even today a final decision. In the first place, it was determined by the earliest authors that the new vessels are outgrowths from the old, and from that time until now this view has received every kind of confirmation. Buds are formed, which shoot out laterally from the vessel wall, and gradually increase in length; similar buds given off from other vessels grow to meet these, and coalesce with them. The buds are at first solid; but they subsequently become tunnelled, while those portions of the vessel wall from which they have grown undergo liquefaction; and in this way new vascular offsets and loops arise. The fine vessels first formed are always capillaries, and are chiefly, though not exclusively, outgrowths from true capillaries. Later on they gradually become wider and acquire thicker walls, and may thus be transformed into vessels of large size. Such being the origin of the new vessels, the source of their blood-supply is at once evident; from the general circulation blood passes out of the old into the new channels."

Lymphatics also grow into healing areas in a similar way. Fortunately (and mysteriously) blood vessel sprouts do not link up with lymphatic sprouts. What stimulates this inward growth of new vessels? It is possible that some factor akin to Judah Folkman's "tumor angiogenesis factor" (thought to induce vascular growth in tumors) may be involved, but no evidence is yet available.

The work of the macrophages is very important because both the injurious agent and the inflammatory reaction leave a lot of debris that must be actively removed. The fibrin, for example, must by lysed or phagocytized. It is interesting to see what happens if the macrophages are prevented from doing their job. Russell Ross and his collaborators studied wound healing in animals treated with antimacrophage serum, and found that, although macrophages are almost entirely absent, wound healing takes place anyway; but the area remains cluttered with debris.

The fibroblasts are busy laying down structural materials (collagen, elastin, ground substance) giving body and strength to the new tissue. But they do more; a few years ago we found that they actually "pull together" the granulation tissue in which they lie, causing it to shrink. It had long been known that gaping wounds tend to close up, and that a characteristic of chronic inflammatory foci is a local contraction; but the force responsible for this shrinkage had not been understood. There were reasons to believe that the fibroblasts were responsible, although it was not understood how they could develop a tension. The first step was therefore to find out, with the electron microscope, whether they showed any evidence of having contracted. Remembering the shriveled nuclei which had been a clue to demonstrating contractility of certain endothelial cells, we looked at the nuclei of the fibroblasts in granulation tissue. In sharp contrast with the nuclei of normal, resting fibroblasts, which were smoothly oval (Figure 90), those of granulation tissue were often deeply indented (Figure 91). Furthermore, the fibroblasts of granulation tissue had developed internal bundles of fibrils (Figures 92, 93) closely similar to the fibrils of smooth muscle cells. In fact, the similarity included the "dense bodies" characteristically found in smooth muscle cells. Some of these bundles appeared to be lined up in series with extracellular fibrous structures resembling "microtendons" (Figure 93). We also found junctions between such fibroblasts. All this is suggestive of a contractile system, whereby the fibroblasts join up and pull onto each other as well as onto the stroma.

Real proof of this contraction could be provided, of course, only by functional studies. We had to demonstrate that these cells, which looked contractile, were actually able to contract. What kind of experiment would you propose to solve this problem? We went about it by taking strips of granulation tissue and using them as strips of smooth muscle suspended in a warm bath and hooked up to a kymograph. These strips responded by contraction to the same group of chemical agents that caused smooth muscle to contract, such as serotonin and bradykinin (Figure 94). As you may expect, the strips could also be induced to relax with smooth-muscle-relaxing agents such as papaverine (Figure 94). The overall change in length was of the order of 5% to 20%.

We also found (thanks to a medical student, now Dr. Bernard Hirschel) that the contractile material within the fibroblasts was immunologically similar to the contractile material in smooth muscle cells. The key to this finding was offered by a peculiar phenomenon. Some patients with chronic hepatitis acquire in their serum (for unknown reasons) an antibody against smooth muscle. This antibody does no apparent harm, but it happens to be a

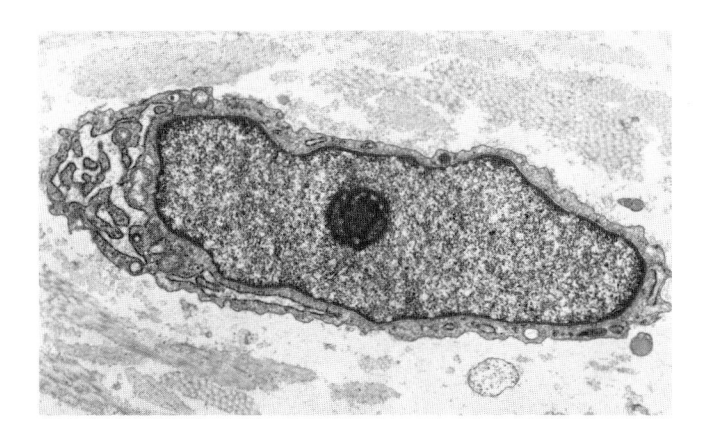

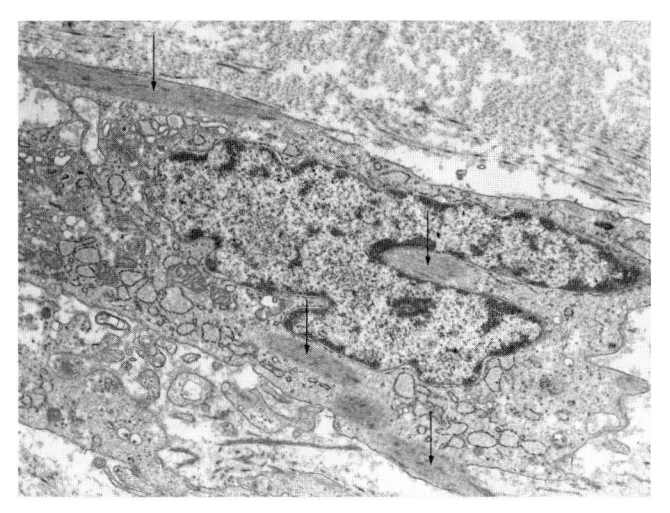

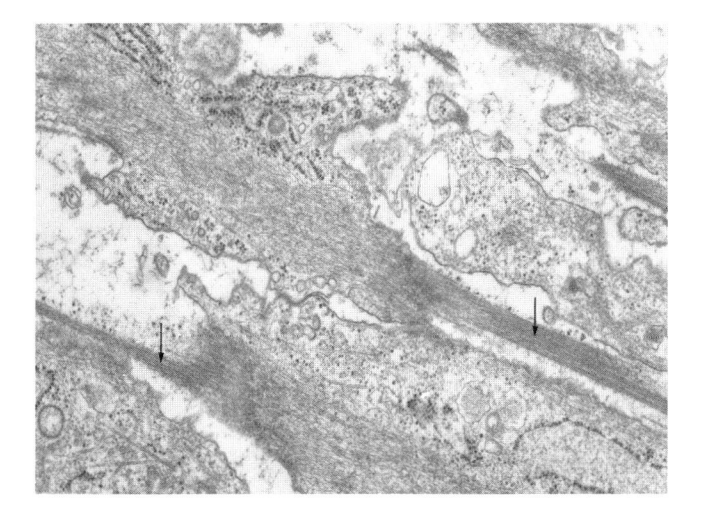

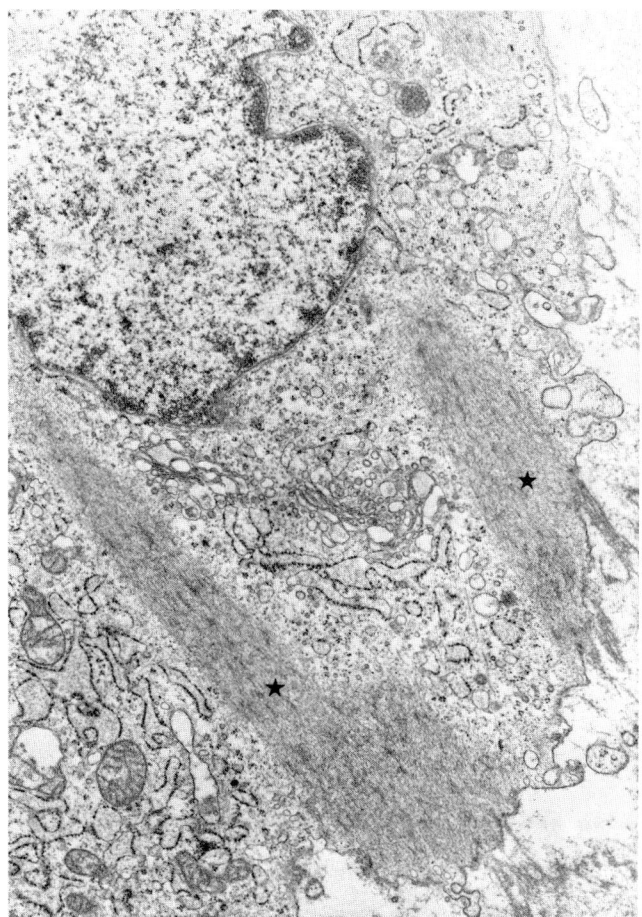

Figure 90. (top left) Normal, resting fibroblast in human skin. Note oval nucleus and abundant rough endoplasmic reticulum.

Figure 91. (middle left) Fibroblast (myofibroblast) from human granulation tissue. Note indented nucleus and prominent bundles of cytoplasmic fibrils (arrows).

Figure 92. (top right) Higher power view of bundles of cytoplasmic fibrils (stars) in myofibroblast from human granulation tissue.

Figure 93. (bottom left) Portions of two myofibroblasts, showing cytoplasmic fibrils and extracellular "microtendons" (arrows).

Figure 94. Kymograph curves obtained with strips of granulation tissue. *Top:* Rat granuloma pouch. 5-hydroxytryptamine (5-HT) induced the strip to contract, papaverine made it relax. *Bottom:* Rat skin wound. Bradykinin induced contraction, papaverine caused relaxation.

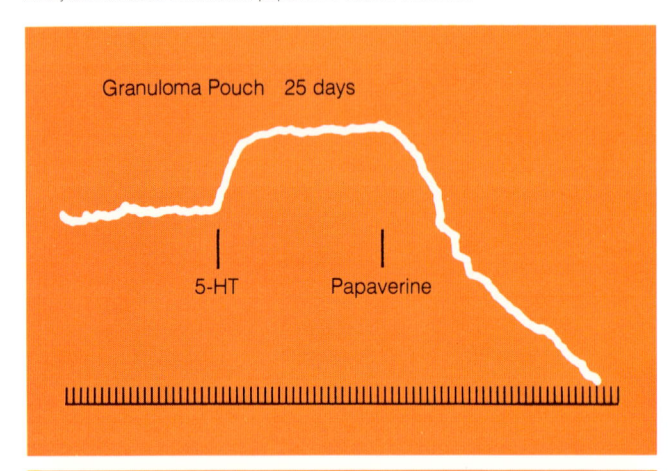

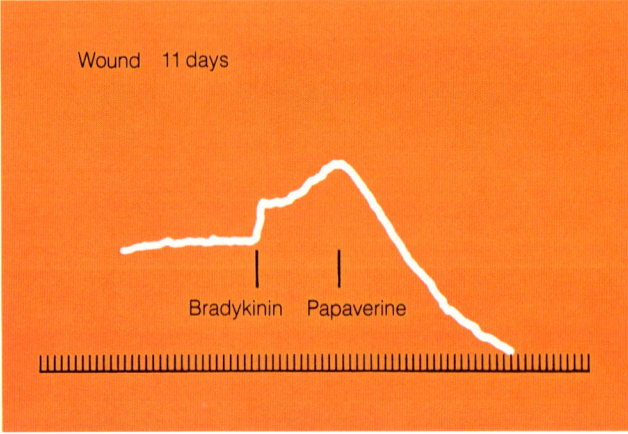

useful tool for the study of smooth muscle cells; it can be applied to sections of fresh tissue and then demonstrated by the standard immunofluorescent technique, whereby normal smooth muscle cells show yellow fluorescence (Figure 95). Normal fibroblasts are not fluorescent with this serum, but fibroblasts in wounds or granulation tissue become as fluorescent as smooth muscle cells (Figure 96, 97). We, therefore, felt justified to propose a new name for this special kind of fibroblast, which appears in an area of injury and modulates in the direction of smooth muscle cells: the *myofibroblast.*

On second thought, these findings could have been made many years ago. Just look at the histologic aspect of the granulation tissue that lines the bottom of a gaping wound in Figure 98. If you had no caption beneath the figure, would you not label it as a section of smooth muscle?

Wound Healing

At this point you are ready to understand the process of wound healing.

Let us assume the situation of a surgical wound that is immediately sutured. The knife has injured millions of cells, including mast cells and vessels; blood was spilled, and a thin clot fills the slit between the apposed margins of the wound. Amines and other mediators have been set free or are newly formed locally, and they immediately induce an acute inflammatory reaction. Plasma seeps into the tissues; and there, with a delay of a few hours, it begins to attract polymorphs. In the absence of significant bacterial contamination, this leukocytic infiltration will be mild and will fade away rapidly. This process amounts to a short phase of aseptic acute inflammation. In the meantime, macrophages that came in with the polymorphs (and a few others that were already there before) work to remove the red blood cells, fibrin, dead polymorphs, and other cellular material. The fibroblasts begin to hypertrophy, and within a day or two they will be seen to multiply on either side of the wound, then to migrate into it. Collagen fibers (and a few elastic fibers) will be laid down, while capillary sprouts will begin to appear on either side of the wound. Somehow, these sprouts will be guided to meet end to end, and within a few days the circulation is reestablished across the margins of the wound.

For the first week or so, the injured zone remains rather rich in cells (especially macrophages and fibroblasts); but as days go by the cellular population decreases and intercellular material increases. *This is a general rule: many cells = young lesion; much collagen = old lesion.*

Along the surface, a linear scab of dried blood has formed; the epithelial cells on both margins undergo mitoses, and then migrate over the wound, creeping beneath the scab. Eventually the scab, being undercut, falls off. Epithelial bridging of a linear wound may take as little as two days.

Suture threads cause a foreign body reaction (giant cells!) and an intense fibrous reaction develops around them; this adds strength to the final scar. However, if bacteria find their way along the thread and into the tissue, pus will form, and healing is delayed until the infection has abated. Healing will also be delayed a) if there is poor blood circulation to the area, as happens in the case of varicose ulceration of the legs, b) if the patient is poor-

Figure 95a. (top) Arteriole in the wall of the rat cecum (hematoxylin and eosin stain). Note fibroblasts at right of vessel, and smooth muscle at lower left.

Figure 95b. (middle) The same field in a section treated with human anti-smooth-muscle antibody and then revealed by an immunofluorescent technique. Contractile structures appear bright yellow-green; the fibroblasts remain invisible.

Figure 96. (bottom) Myofibroblasts from the bottom of a skin wound treated with anti-smooth-muscle antibody as in Figure 94. Note the bright fluorescence, indicating the presence of intracellular contractile structures.

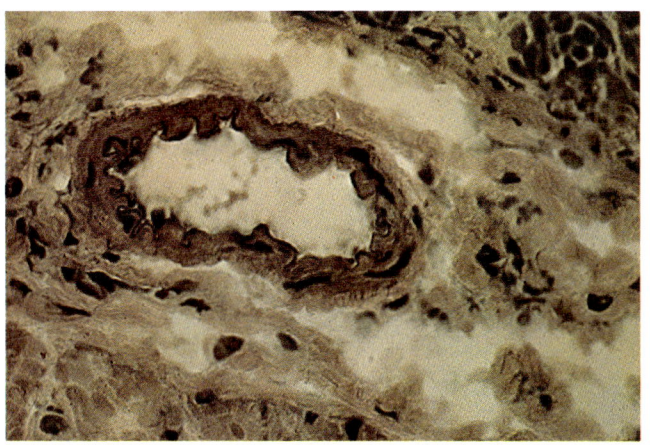

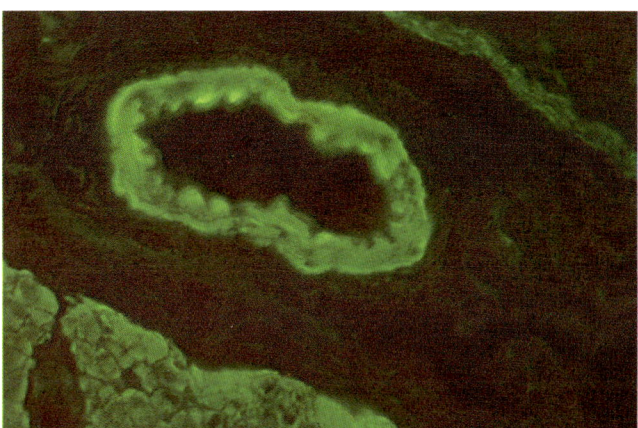

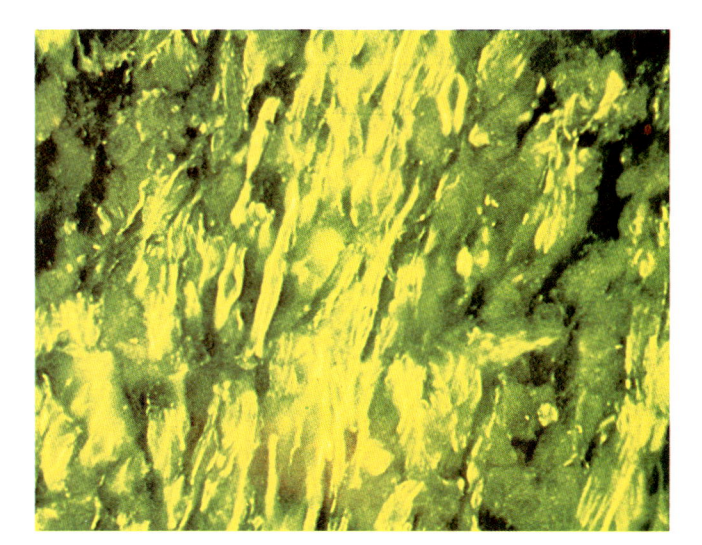

Figure 97. Top: Tissue culture of fibroblasts treated with normal human serum; there is no specific fluorescence. This is a control procedure. *Bottom:* Tissue culture of fibroblasts treated with anti-smooth-muscle antibody. The brightly fluorescent streaks represent contractile material.

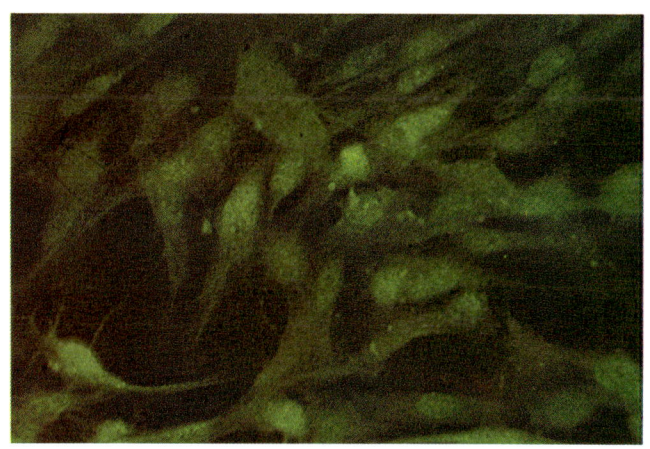

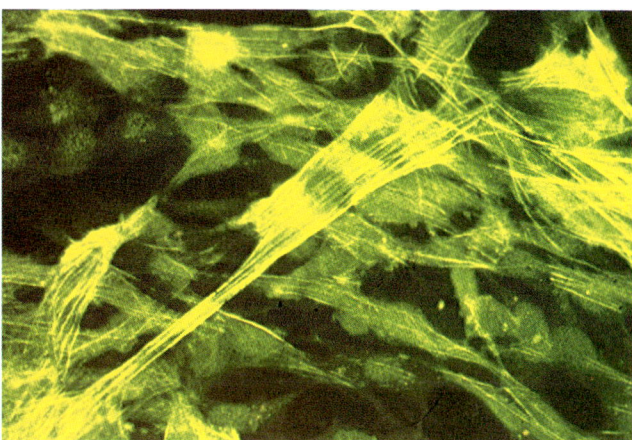

ly nourished (particularly in ascorbic acid deficiency, "scurvy," in which there is defective collagen synthesis) or c) if the patient is being treated with cortisone (which apparently suppresses the proliferation of fibroblasts).

On the skin the scar of a surgical wound may be fairly obvious, but the repair in the subcutaneous tissue beneath it is usually so good (with so little scar tissue remaining) that even under the microscope it may be difficult to find. If visible, it will appear as a thin, fibrous streak, descending from the skin. Scar tissue in striated muscle remains very obvious.

This sequence of wound healing, occurring in the absence of infection, goes under the ancient name of *healing by first intention*. If infection does occur, there will be an initial phase of suppuration. As long as this lasts, no healing will occur, but the closing process will resume as soon

Inflammation – A Two-Edged Sword

Figure 98. Left: Normal connective tissue from the dermis of a rabbit. *Right:* Granulation tissue from the bottom of an 11-day-old wound in the same rabbit. The transformation of the fibroblasts is striking.

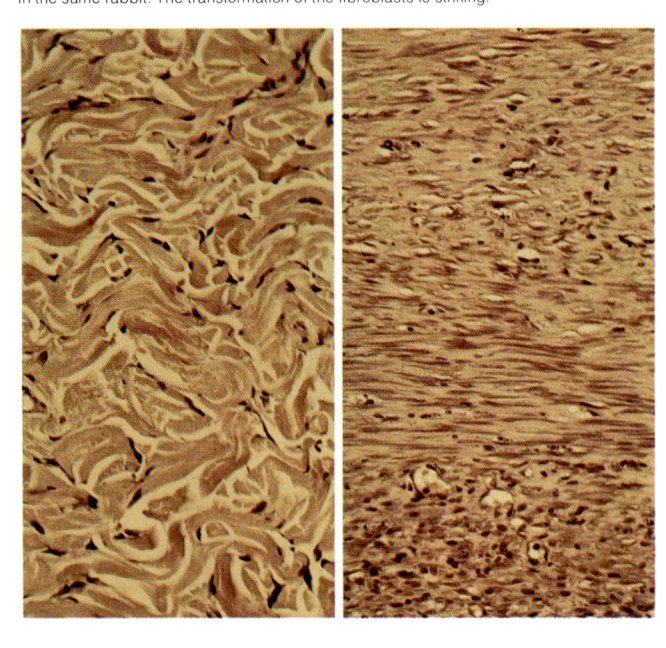

as the infection is overcome. This is called *healing by second intention.*

If the wound is not sutured, but left gaping, the initial part of the sequence is essentially the same, but the exposed bottom of the wound will fill up with new connective tissue – granulation tissue. This will slowly contract and pull the margins together. If the gap is not too great, the contraction alone will suffice; in other cases, the remaining gap is closed by epithelialization (the epidermis spreads to cover the granulation tissue). An odd phenomenon is that the contractile tissue, made up of myofibroblasts, disappears after it has done its job; most of its cells simply vanish, leaving a collagenous scar. This is merely one of the unknowns of wound healing.

Also unknown is the mechanism that causes a fibroblast to modulate into a myofibroblast. But the overall process of repair (including wound healing) begins to appear as one of the most beautiful biologic processes. Notice that the same mediator substances that cause arterioles to dilate (bringing more blood to the injured area) also cause the venules to leak (bringing antibodies and helping to wash away injurious products); at least one of them, serotonin, causes fibroblasts to proliferate; and they also cause the myofibroblasts to contract, thereby "closing the chapter:" truly a marvel of coordination.

Now that we have described the inflammatory process and its sequelae, let us briefly consider its role (and effects) in clinical medicine. There is little doubt that the inflammatory response is designed to do two particular jobs: *a)* to rid the body of foreign invaders, particularly microbes; and *b)* to effectively dispose of damaged tissue, thus allowing healing to occur. Therefore, inflammation occurs in response to all kinds of infection (with bacteria, viruses, fungi, etc.), and all kinds of tissue damage, burns, chemical injury, infarction, etc.

Sometimes it seems that the inflammatory response is not quite up to the task. For instance, when pyogenic bacteria are not immediately killed, an abscess forms; when irritants in general are allowed to persist in the tissues, chronic inflammation develops.

In particular circumstances, *inflammation apparently does more harm than good*. When inflammation affects a joint (such as in rheumatoid arthritis), the cartilage can be damaged by neutrophil lysosomal enzymes that enter the area. This leads to a vicious circle of repeated injury and persistent inflammation (Figure 99). Eventually, severe deformity results from progressive destruction of the joint (Figure 99). Research in this field is being carried out at three main levels: *First,* what is the causative agent? In rheumatoid arthritis, it is suspected that immunologic mechanisms are involved. Immune complexes are detectable in rheumatoid synovial fluid, but the nature of the antigenic stimulus is unknown. *Secondly,* can lysosomal enzyme-mediated damage be minimized either by limiting the number of neutrophils that enter the joint, or by preventing enzyme release from the neutrophils? In the latter area, efforts are being made to work out how lysosomal discharge occurs, and whether the lysosomal membrane can be "stabilized." *Thirdly,* how do the so-called anti-inflammatory drugs operate? These agents include aspirin and the aspirin-like drugs (indomethacin, phenylbutazone) and the adrenocorticosteroids. We mentioned earlier that aspirin and aspirin-like drugs inhibit prostaglandin synthesis; this could affect mediator production or cellular processes that are regulated by cyclic AMP levels. Steroid hormones have been claimed to have a host of effects; the most significant in this context is probably the stabilization of lysosomal membranes.

In the renal glomerulus, inflammation ("glomerulonephritis") can result from the local deposition of immune complexes. This induces injury to the glomerular capillary walls (revealed by the presence of plasma proteins and blood cells in the urine). If the degree of injury is sufficiently severe or if chronic inflammation develops, resolution cannot occur and the glomerulus is eventually replaced by fibrous tissue. If many glomeruli are affected, this change can lead to renal insufficiency, yet another unfortunate effect of the inflammatory process and its sequelae.

Inflammation can occur in the walls of blood vessels, "vasculitis." For example, "arteritis" can result from the deposition of antigen-antibody complexes in the wall. "Phlebitis" usually results from local injury or infection of a vein (sometimes from a tube placed in the lumen). The most serious consequence of vasculitis is endothelial injury, which predisposes the patient to local thrombosis (with the attendant dangers of embolism and infarction).

The process of repair can sometimes cause serious problems. We have discussed the contraction of granulation tissue and its useful role in helping to close a wound. In some situations, however, this phenomenon can have disastrous consequences for the patient. In burns, it can cause disfigurement. It can immobilize joints. In the peritoneal cavity, it can cause bowel obstruction. Inside the heart (following the endocarditis of rheumatic fever) it can shrink and deform valves (Figure 100). Presently, we do not know how to prevent this side effect of repair. Obviously this will be an important topic for future research.

Inflammation and Cancer

The role of inflammation in the cause or prevention of cancer has been debated for years. It is extremely unlikely that inflammation *per se* can cause cancer. The tumors that seem to arise (rarely) in chronically inflamed lesions, as in long-standing ulcerations of the stomach, colon, and perhaps the skin, probably result rather from the continued damage and attempted regeneration in the local cells of the area. Indeed, the available evidence suggests that inflammation may act to *limit* tumors. It has been proposed for example, that the infiltration of inflammatory cells in breast tumors may be a good prognostic sign, suggesting that spread of malignant cells

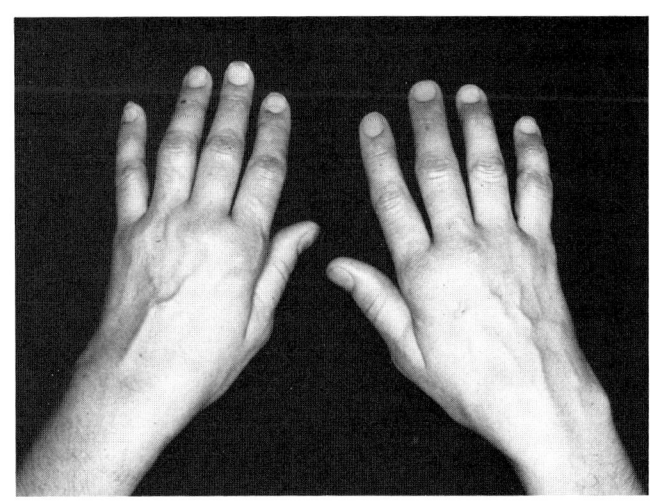

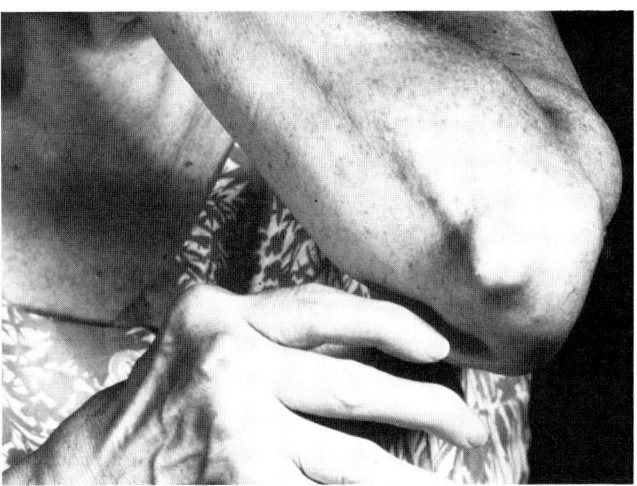

Figure 99. Top: Hand inflammation in early rheumatoid arthritis is characterized by bilateral and symmetrical swelling of the proximal interphalangeal, metacarpophalangeal, and wrist joints.
Bottom: Hand deformities in rheumatoid arthritis with permanent flexion contractures and ulnar deviation. Note subcutaneous nodules over knuckles and at the elbow, which impart a poor prognosis.

Conclusion

may be reduced. Recent work by François Jacob's group in Paris bears directly on this point. They found that tumor cells release a factor that *prevents* inflammation (in particular, leukocytic infiltration). In addition, macrophages did not attach themselves to such tumor cells *in vitro*, whereas they did attach to normal cells. In combination, these effects could be advantageous for malignant cells, allowing them to become established in the tissues and to grow into tumors. An interesting parallel was drawn when this same group showed that macrophages did not attach to trophoblast cells; hence, the speculation that similar mechanisms might explain the lack of inflammation that accompanies trophoblastic invasion of the uterine decidua during pregnancy. We expect further developments in this exciting area.

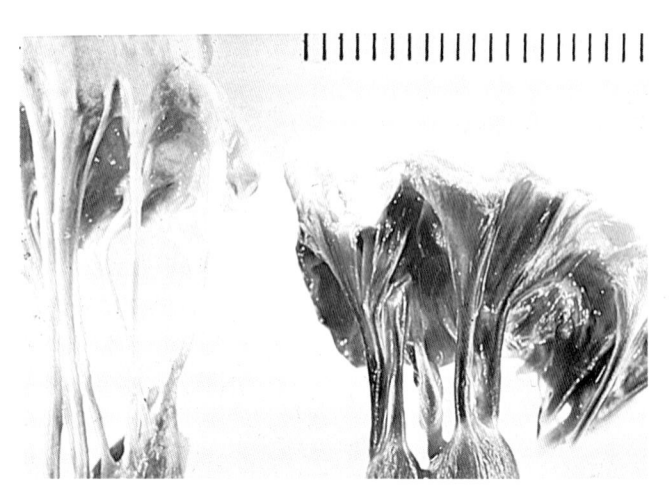

Figure 100. Left: Part of a normal atrioventricular valve from a human heart. Note the long, slender chordae tendineae. *Right:* Similar apparatus from the heart of a patient who had suffered from rheumatic fever. Inflammation of the endocardium has resulted in shortening and thickening of the chordae tendineae.

Let us conclude with a brief overview of the inflammatory process (Figure 101). When tissues are injured, mast cells (and probably other cells) quickly release mediators that cause vasodilatation and vascular leakage. (The mast cell acts as a "sentinel" out in the tissues; it sounds the alarm to the endothelial cells standing around the perimeter of the "fort," the blood vessel wall.) Leakage can also occur if there is direct injury to the vessel. An inflammatory "soup" then simmers away in the tissues, with ingredients being added from exuding plasma and damaged cells. These ingredients provoke more vascular leakage and attract leukocytes out of the venules. The leukocytes phagocytize bacteria and mop up cellular debris. Lymphocytes come in if a cell-mediated immunologic process is involved. Mediators can also enter the circulation and cause general effects, such as fever. If the irritant persists, the process will become chronic (usually with crowds of macrophages). Otherwise, the reaction will settle down; if there is significant tissue damage, repair occurs with new blood vessels, proliferation of fibroblasts, and the formation of scar tissue.

For our "last word," we cannot improve on Julius Cohnheim's:

"We have now completed our discussion of inflammation. I have attempted to lay before you in detail the peculiarities of the circulatory disturbance on which this process depends; I have enumerated the causes capable of producing the disturbance so far as they are at present known, and I have, in conclusion, dealt with the subsequent destiny of the inflammatory products. Throughout the entire exposition I have, I believe, clearly distinguished between what has already been added by observation and experiment to the body of thoroughly established scientific fact, and what is still of a hypothetical character. Nor, I think, have I concealed from you how great and palpable are the gaps in many portions of this subject. I need only mention, e.g., the inadequacy of our knowledge with regard to the nature of the changes in the vessel walls as well as of the chemical processes taking place in the exudations. But whatever I may have said, it was with the events occurring in connection with the circulation and transudation that I chiefly concerned myself; and the retrogressive, and more especially the regenerative, processes taking place in the tissues and their elements during inflammation should, I considered, be introduced only on practical grounds, because of their nearly constant association with the inflammatory process proper."

Figure 101. Summary of the principal mechanisms of the inflammatory reaction.

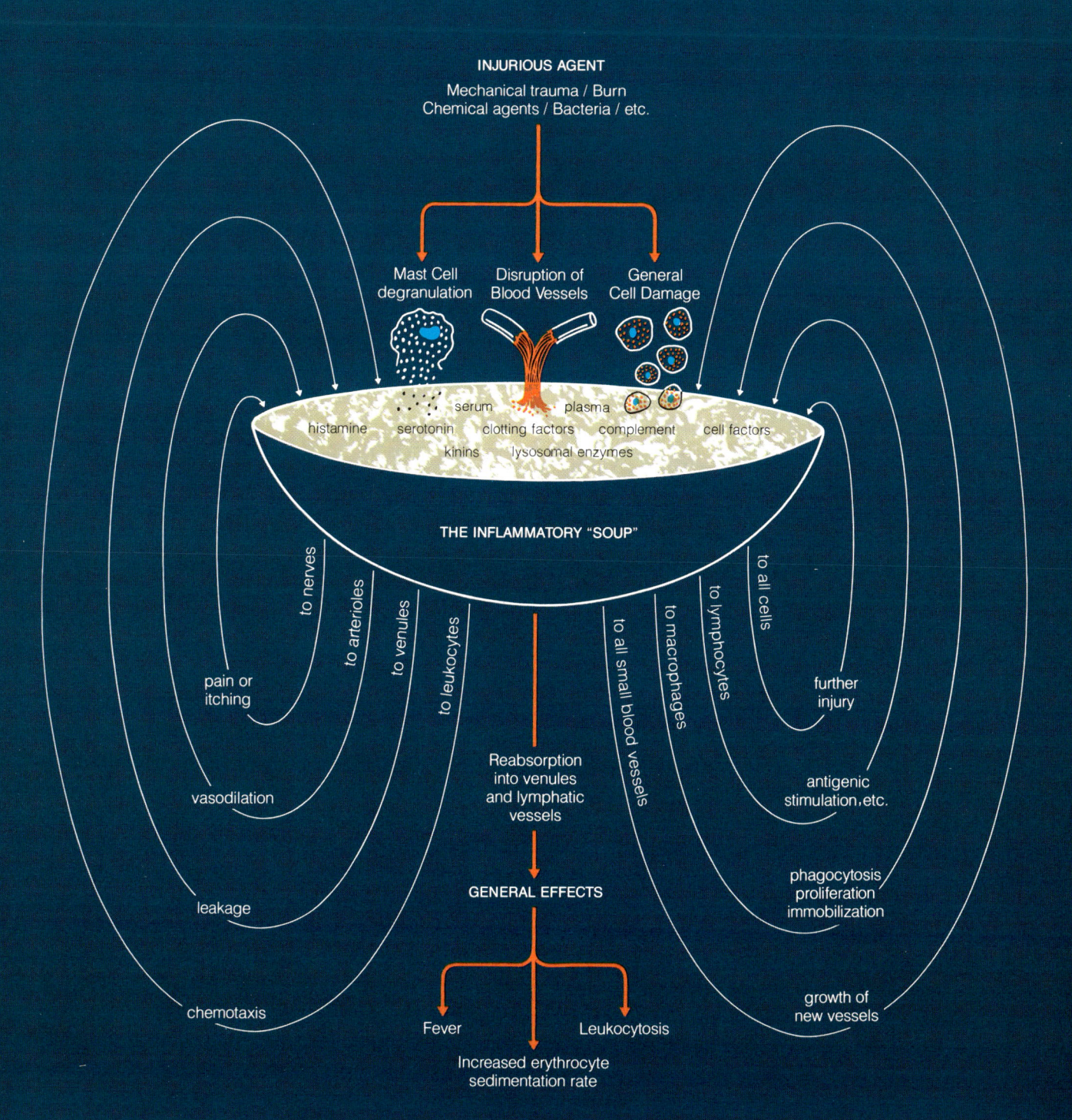

Bibliography

General Reading (These books contain useful references for each section):

Florey Lord (ed): **General Pathology**, 4th edition. Philadelphia and London, WB Saunders Company, 1970.

Hurley JV: **Acute Inflammation**. Edinburgh and London, Churchill Livingstone, 1972.

Lepow IH, Ward PA (eds): **Inflammation: Mechanisms and Control**. New York and London, Academic Press, 1972.

Movat HZ (ed): **Inflammation, Immunity and Hypersensitivity**. New York, Harper and Row, 1971.

Thomas L, Uhr JW, Grant L (eds): **International Symposium on Injury, Inflammation and Immunity**. Baltimore, The Williams and Wilkins Company, 1964.

Zweifach BW, Grant L, McCluskey RT (eds): **The Inflammatory Process**, 2nd edition, Volumes I, II and III. New York and London, Academic Press, 1974.

Historic Highlights:

Majno G: **The Healing Hand. Man and Wound in the Ancient World**. Cambridge, Harvard University Press, 1975.

The Acute Inflammatory Response:

Cohnheim J: **Lectures in General Pathology**, 2nd edition. Volume 1 (translated from the 2nd German edition). London, The New Sydenham Society, 1889.

Increased Vascular Permeability:

Cotran RS, Majno G: A light and electron microscopic analysis of vascular injury. **Ann NY Acad Sci** 116:750-763, 1964.

Hurley JV, Edwards B, Ham KN: The response of newly formed blood vessels in healing wounds to histamine and other permeability factors. **Pathology** 2:133-145, 1970.

Hurley JV, Ham KN, Ryan GB: The mechanism of the delayed prolonged phase of increased vascular permeability in mild thermal injury in the rat. **J Pathol** 94:1-12, 1967.

Joris I, Majno G, Ryan GB: Endothelial contraction *in vivo*: a study of the rat mesentery. **Virchows Arch** [Zellpathol] 12:73-83, 1972.

Karnovsky MJ: The ultrastructural basis of capillary permeability studied with peroxidase as a tracer. **J Cell Biol** 35:213-236, 1967.

Landis EM, Pappenheimer JR: Exchange of substances through the capillary walls. In WF Hamilton, P Dow (eds): **Handbook of Physiology**, Section 2, Volume II. Washington, American Physiological Society, 1963, p 961-1043.

Leak LV, Burke JF: Ultrastructural studies on the lymphatic anchoring filaments. **J Cell Biol** 36:129-149, 1968.

Majno G: Ultrastructure of the vascular membrane, in WF Hamilton, P Dow (eds): **Handbook of Physiology**, Section 2, Volume III. Washington, American Physiological Society, 1965, pp 2293-2375.

Majno G, Palade GE: Studies on inflammation. I. The effect of histamine and serotonin on vascular permeability: an electron microscopic study. **J Biophys Biochem Cytol** 11:571-605, 1961.

Majno G, Palade GE, Schoefl G: I. Studies on inflammation, II. The site of action of histamine and serotonin along the vascular tree: a topographic study. **J Biophys Biochem Cytol** 11:607-626, 1961.

Majno G, Shea SM, Leventhal M: Endothelial contraction induced by histamine-type mediators: an electron microscopic study. **J Cell Biol** 42:647-672, 1969.

Pullinger BD, Florey HW: Some observations on the structure and function of lymphatics: their behavior in local edema. **Br J Exp Pathol** 16:49-61, 1935.

Simionescu N, Simionescu M, Palade GE: Permeability of muscle capillaries to small heme-peptides. Evidence for the existence of patent transendothelial channels. **J Cell Biol** 64:586-607, 1975.

Leukocytic Infiltration:

Bessis M: Studies on cell agony and death: An attempt at classification, in AVS de Reuck and J Knight (eds): **Cellular Injury** (Ciba Foundation Symposium). London, Churchill, 1964, pp 287-316.

Boyden S: Chemotactic effect of mixtures of antibody and antigen on polymorphonuclear leukocytes. **J Exp Med** 115:453-466, 1962.

Buckley IK: Delayed secondary damage and leucocyte chemotaxis following focal aseptic heat injury *in vivo*. **Exp Mol Pathol** 2:402-417, 1963.

Giddon DB, Lindhe J: *In vivo* quantitation of local anesthetic suppression of leukocyte adherence. **Am J Pathol** 68:327-338, 1972.

Harris H: Chemotaxis of granulocytes. **J Pathol Bacteriol** 66:135-146, 1953.

Hurley JV: Incubation of serum with tissue extracts as a cause of chemotaxis of granulocytes. **Nature** 198:1212-1213, 1963.

Hurley JV: Acute inflammation: the effect of concurrent leucocytic emigration and increased permeability on particle retention by the vascular wall. **Br J Exp Pathol** 45:627-633, 1964.

Hurley JV: Substances promoting leukocyte emigration. **Ann NY Acad Sci** 116:918-935, 1964.

Hurley JV, Ryan GB, Friedman A: The mononuclear response to intrapleural injecton in the rat. **J Pathol Bacteriol** 91:575-587, 1966.

Hurley JV, Spector WG: Endogenous factors responsible for leucocytic emigration *in vivo*. **J Pathol Bacteriol** 82:403-420, 1961.

Luft JH: Fine structure of capillary and endocapillary layer as revealed by ruthenium red. **Fed Proc** 25:1773-1783, 1966.

Marchesi VT: The site of leucocyte emigration during inflammation. **Q J Exp Physiol** 46:115-118, 1961.

Marchesi VT, Florey HW: Electron micrographic observations on the emigration of leucocytes. **Q J Exp Physiol** 45:343-348, 1960.

Ryan GB: The origin and sequence of the cells found in the acute inflammatory response. **Aust J Exp Biol Med Sci** 45:149-162, 1967.

Ryan GB, Hurley JV: The chemotaxis of polymorphonuclear leucocytes towards damaged tissue. **Br J Exp Pathol** 47:530-536, 1966.

Schoefl G: I. The migration of lymphocytes across the vascular endothelium in lymphoid tissue. A reexamination. **J Exp Med** 136:568-588, 1972.

Thompson PL, Papadimitriou JM, Walters MNI: Suppression of leukocytic sticking and emigration by chelation of calcium. **J Pathol Bacteriol** 94:389-396, 1967.

Wilkinson PC: **Chemotaxis and Inflammation**. Edinburgh and London, Churchill Livingstone, 1974.

Zigmond SH: Mechanisms of sensing chemical gradients by polymorphonuclear leukocytes. **Nature** 249:450-452, 1974.

Zigmond SH, Hirsch JG: Leukocyte locomotion and chemotaxis. New methods for evaluation, and demonstration of a cell-derived chemotactic factor. **J Exp Med** 137:387-410, 1973.

Phagocytosis:

Bellanti JA, Dayton DH (eds.): **The Phagocytic Cell in Host Resistance.** New York, Raven Press, 1975.

Karnovsky ML: Metabolic basis of phagocytic activity. **Physiol Rev** 42:143-168, 1962.

Klebanoff SJ: Iodination of bacteria: a bactericidal mechanism. **J Exp Med** 126:1063-1078, 1967.

Klebanoff SJ: Intraleukocytic microbicidal defects. **Annu Rev Med** 22:39-62, 1971.

Metchnikoff E: **Immunity in Infective Diseases.** London, Cambridge University Press, 1905.

Metchnikoff O: **Life of Elie Metchnikoff 1845-1916.** Boston and New York, Houghton Mifflin Company, 1921.

Stossel TP: Phagocytosis. **N Engl J Med** 290:717-723; 774-780; 833-839, 1974.

Van Furth R (ed.): **Mononuclear Phagocytes.** Oxford and Edinburgh, Blackwell Scientific Publications, 1970.

Williams RC Jr, Fudenberg HH (eds.): **Phagocytic Mechanisms in Health and Disease.** New York, Intercontinental Medical Book Corporation, 1972.

Wright AE, Douglas SR: Further observations on the role of the blood fluids in connection with phagocytosis. **Proc Roy Soc (Lond)** 73:128-142, 1904.

Defects of Leukocytic Function:

Baehner RL: Molecular basis for functional disorders of phagocytes. **J Pediatr** 84:317-327, 1974.

Holmes B, Quie PG, Windhorst DB, Good RA: Fatal granulomatous disease of childhood: An inborn abnormality of phagocytic function. **Lancet** 1:1225-1228, 1966.

Johnston RB Jr, Baehner RL: Improvement of leukocyte bactericidal activity in chronic granulomatous disease. **Blood** 35:350-355, 1970.

Karnovsky ML: Chronic granulomatous disease — pieces of a cellular and molecular puzzle. **Fed Proc** 32:1527-1533, 1973.

Segal AW: Nitroblue-tetrazolium tests. **Lancet** 2:1248-1252, 1974.

Ward PA: Leukotaxis and leukotactic disorders. **Am J Pathol** 77:520-538, 1974.

Mediators of Inflammation:

Allison AC, Harington JS, Birbeck M: An examination of the cytotoxic effects of silica on macrophages. **J Exp Med** 124:141-153, 1966.

Amos B (ed.): **Progress in Immunology, First International Congress of Immunology.** New York and London, Academic Press, 1971.

Austen KF, Becker EL (eds.): **Biochemistry of the Acute Allergic Reactions, Second International Symposium.** Oxford and Edinburgh, Blackwell Scientific Publications, 1971.

Bourne HR, Lichtenstein LM, Melmon KL, et al: Modulation of inflammation and immunity by cyclic AMP. **Science** 184:19-28, 1974.

Brocklehurst WE: The release of histamine and formation of a slow-reacting substance (SRS-A) during anaphylactic shock. **J Physiol** 151:416-435, 1960.

Cochrane CG: Immunologic tissue injury mediated by neutrophilic leukocytes. **Adv Immunol** 9:97-162, 1968.

David JR: Lymphocyte mediators and cellular hypersensitivity. **N Engl J Med** 288:143-149, 1973.

David JR, David RR: Cellular hypersensitivity and immunity. Inhibition of macrophage migration and the lymphocyte mediators. **Prog Allergy** 16:300-449, 1972.

Donaldson VH, Evans RR: A biochemical abnormality in hereditary angioneurotic edema. Absence of serum inhibitor of C'1 esterase. **Am J Med** 35:37-44, 1963.

Henson PM: Pathologic mechanisms in neutrophil-mediated injury. **Am J Pathol** 68:593-612, 1972.

Janoff A: Neutrophil proteases in inflammation. **Annu Rev Med** 23:177-190, 1972.

Lewis T: **The Blood Vessels of the Human Skin and Their Responses.** London, Shaw and Sons Ltd, 1927.

Lundh B, Laurell A-B, Wetterqvist H, et al: A case of hereditary angioneurotic oedema, successfully treated with ε-aminocaproic acid. Studies on C'esterase inhibitor, C'1 activation, plasminogen level and histamine metabolism. **Clin Exp Immunol** 3:733-745, 1968.

Margolis J: Hageman factor and capillary permeability. **Aust J Exp Biol Med Sci** 37:239-244, 1959.

Miles AD: The kinin system. A history and review of the kinin system. **Proc Roy Soc Lond Biol** 173:341-349, 1969.

Miles AA, Wilhelm DL: Enzyme-like globulins from serum reproducing the vascular phenomena of inflammation. I. An activable permeability factor and its inhibitor in guinea pig serum. **Br J Exp Pathol** 36:71-81, 1955.

Müller-Eberhard HJ: Complement. **Annu Rev Biochem** 38:389-414, 1969.

Orange RP, Austen KF: Slow reacting substance of anaphylaxis. **Adv Immunol** 10:105-144, 1969.

Osler AG, Sandberg AL: Alternate complement pathways. **Prog Allergy** 17:51-92, 1973.

Pike JE: Prostaglandins. **Sci Am** 225(5):84-92, 1971.

Pillemer L, Blum L, Lepow IH, et al: The properdin system and immunity. I. Demonstration and isolation of a new serum protein, properdin, and its role in immune phenomena. **Science** 120:279-285, 1954.

Ratnoff OD: A tangled web. The interdependence of mechanisms of blood clotting, fibrinolysis, immunity and inflammation. **Thromb Diath Haemorrh Suppl** 45:109-118, 1971.

Ryan GB: Mediators of inflammation. **Beitr Pathol** 152:272-291, 1974.

Snyderman R, Phillips J, Mergenhagen SE: Polymorphonuclear leukocyte chemotactic activity in rabbit serum and guinea pig serum treated with immune complexes: evidence for C5a as the major chemotactic factor. **Infect Immun** 1:521-525, 1970.

Stecher VJ, Sorkin E: Studies on chemotaxis. XII. Generation of chemotactic activity for polymorphonuclear leucocytes in sera with complement deficiencies. **Immunology** 16:231-239, 1969.

Vane JR: Inhibition of prostaglandin synthesis as a mechanism of action for aspirin-like drugs. **Nature [New Biol]** 231:232-235, 1971.

Ward PA: Complement-derived leukotactic factors in pathological fluids. **J Exp Med** 134:109s-113s, 1971.

Ward PA: Leukotactic factors in health and disease. **Am J Pathol** 64:521-530, 1971.

Ward PA, Cochrane CG, Müller-Eberhard HJ: Further studies on the chemotactic factor of complement and its formation *in vivo*. **Immunology** 11:141-153, 1966.

Weissman G, Rita GA: Molecular basis of gouty inflammation: interaction of monosodium urate crystals with lysosomes and liposomes. **Nature [New Biol]** 240:167-172, 1972.

Wilhelm DL: Kinins in human disease. **Annu Rev Med** 22:63-84, 1971.

Chronic Inflammation:

Ryan GB, Spector WG: Macrophage turnover in inflamed connective tissue. **Proc Roy Soc Lond Biol** 174:269-292, 1970.

Spector WG: The macrophage: its origin and role in pathology, in HL Ioachim (ed): **Pathobiology Annual.** New York, Appleton-Century-Crofts, 1974, pp 33-64.

Unanue ER, Benacerraf B: Immunologic events in experimental hypersensitivity granulomas. **Am J Pathol** 71:349-364, 1973.

Volkman A, Gowans JL: The production of macrophages in the rat. **Br J Exp Pathol** 46:50-61, 1965.

Volkman A, Gowans JL: The origin of macrophages from the bone marrow in the rat. **Br J Exp Pathol** 46:62-70, 1965.

Warren KS: Granulomatous inflammation, in IH Lepow and PA Ward (eds): **Inflammation: Mechanisms and Control.** New York and London, Academic Press, 1972, pp 203-217.

Systemic Effects of Inflammation:

Atkins E, Bodel P: Fever. **N Engl J Med** 286:27-34, 1972.

Golde DW, Cline MJ: Regulation of granulopoiesis. **N Engl J Med** 291:1388-1395, 1974.

Gordon AS (ed.): **Regulation of Haematopoiesis.** New York, Appleton-Century-Crofts, 1970.

Metcalf D, Moore MAS: **Haematopoietic Cells.** Amsterdam, North-Holland Publishing Company, 1971.

Wood WB Jr: The pathogenesis of fever, in S Mudd (ed): **Infectious Agents and Host Reactions.** Philadelphia and London, WB Saunders Company, 1970, pp 146-162.

Inflammation — The Healing Phase:

Folkman J, Merler E, Abernathy C, Williams G: Isolation of a tumor factor responsible for angiogenesis. **J Exp Med** 133:275-288, 1971.

Gabbiani G, Hirschel BJ, Ryan GB, Statkov PR, Majno G: Granulation tissue as a contractile organ. A study of structure and function. **J Exp Med** 135:719-734, 1972.

Leibovich SJ, Ross R: The role of the macrophage in wound repair. A study with hydrocortisone and antimacrophage serum. **Am J Pathol** 78:71-99, 1975.

Ross R: Wound healing. **Sci Am** 220(6):40-50, 1969.

Ryan GB, Cliff WJ, Gabbiani G, Irlé C, Montandon D, Statkov PR, Majno G: Myofibroblasts in human granulation tissue. **Hum Pathol** 5:55-67, 1974.

Schoefl G: I. Studies on inflammation. III. Growing capillaries: their structure and permeability. **Virchow Arch Path Anat** 337:97-141, 1963.

Inflammation — A Two-Edged Sword:

Fauve RM, Hevin B, Jacob H, et al: Antiinflammatory effects of murine malignant cells. **Proc Natl Acad Sci USA** 71:4052-4056, 1974.

Acknowledgments

The authors thank Dr. Isabelle Joris for careful screening of the manuscript and assistance with photomicrography; Mrs. Karen Melia and Mrs. Delwyn Ryan for typing the manuscript; and the following colleagues for kindly providing illustrative material:

Baruj Benacerraf, MD, Department of Pathology, Harvard Medical School, Boston, Mass. (*Figures 84a and 84b*).

Richard T. Briggs, PhD, Department of Pathology, Harvard Medical School, Boston, Mass. (*Figure 42*).

John J. Calabro, MD, Worcester City Hospital, Worcester, Mass. (*Figures 99a and 99b*).

Ramzi S. Cotran, MD, Department of Pathology, Peter Bent Brigham Hospital and Harvard Medical School, Boston, Mass. (*Figure 21*).

James G. Hirsch, MD, Rockefeller University, New York, N.Y. (*Figure 46*).

Isabelle Joris, PhD, Department of Pathology, University of Massachusetts Medical School, Worcester, Mass. (*Figures 15, 18, 34, 35, 36*).

Morris J. Karnovsky, MB, BCh, Department of Pathology, Harvard Medical School, Boston, Mass. (*Figures 7, 28, 29, 30, 31, 42*).

Miss Geneviève Leyvraz, Department of Pathology, University of Geneva, Switzerland (*Figure 26*).

Gutta Schoefl, PhD, Department of Experimental Pathology, The John Curtin School of Medical Research, Australian National University, Canberra, Australia (*Figure 76*).

Emil R. Unanue, MD, Department of Pathology, Harvard Medical School, Boston, Mass. (*Figures 68, 84a and 84b*).

Mrs. Angela Farkas Valu, Department of Pathology, University of Massachusetts Medical School, Worcester, Mass. (*Figure 16*).

Dorothea Zucker-Franklin, MD, Department of Medicine, New York University Medical Center, New York, N.Y. (*Figure 48*).

We also acknowledge the following sources:

Academic Press (*The Inflammatory Process*, 1965, Eds. Zweifach, Grant and McCluskey) (*Figure 46*).

American Journal of Pathology (*Figure 21*).

British Journal of Experimental Pathology (*Figures 40a and 40b*).

Human Pathology (*Figures 90-93*).

Journal of Cell Biology (*Figure 7*).

Macmillan Publishing Company [*Inflammation*, 1907, J. George Adami] (*Figure 43*).

National Library of Medicine, Bethesda, MD (*Figures 2, 4, 33*).

Shaw and Sons [*The Blood Vessels of the Human Skin and Their Responses*, 1927, Thomas Lewis] (*Figures 53a and 53b*).

Virchows Archiv (*Figures 18, 76*).

Michael K. Bach, PhD, The Upjohn Company.
(Cover photograph of Rat Mast Cells).